quite contrary
Dr. Mary Edwards Walker

Other books by the same author

For Teen-Age Readers

LOOK AT ME!

CLOTHESHORSE

A VALENTINE FOR VINNIE

ONE PERFECT ROSE

FANFARE FOR TWO

RITA RINGS A BELL

A HATBOX FOR MIMI

WHITE COLLAR GIRL

For Younger Readers

MYSTERY AT LIONS GATE

THE WHISTLE STOP MYSTERY

Mary E. Walker, M. D.

MARJORY HALL

Quite Contrary
Dr. Mary Edwards Walker

FUNK & WAGNALLS
NEW YORK

Published by Funk & Wagnalls, *A Division of* Reader's Digest Books, Inc.
Library of Congress Catalogue Card Number: 76-100652
Printed in the United States of America
 1

To FRANK WAGGONER
who started it all . . .

contents

quite contrary
Dr. Mary Edwards Walker

1

mary, mary

From the beginning Mary wondered about her name, thinking it both odd and unfair that her sisters had been given what she considered poetic names, while she was forced to wear the commonplace name of Mary.

"Poetic!" said her friend Evvy Barnes scornfully. "I'm glad nobody thought to call me Aurora."

"I think Aurora is a very pretty name. And so are my other sisters' names—they're all pretty."

"Even your brother has a fancy name," Evvy pointed out. "Alvah!"

"It's no funnier than Evvy. Evvy should be short for Evelyn, my mother said so. But just plain Evvy—I think *that's* funny. Alvah is named for Father, and Vesta for Mother."

"They ran out of those fancy names, I guess, when they got to you."

"I was named for Father's sister. She lives in Massachusetts, where he came from. Mother did too."

"And Edwards, Mary Edwards—oh, I suppose Edwards was your mother's name before she was married."

"No, it wasn't," Mary contradicted her. "My mother was a Whitcomb—it's a very famous family back in New England. So is Father's family—very important. No, the Edwards is for Jonathan Edwards. He was a Puritan, a minister, I think, and greatly admired by my father." She stopped talking and wished, for a moment, that her father had admired people such as Evvy would have heard of. Mary Bradford Walker, Mary Standish Walker, Mary Winthrop Walker—any one of them would have been an improvement. Then, sighing, she said, "But, *Mary*. It's so ordinary. It isn't like my family at all."

"My father says your whole family is—different," Evvy said, hesitating before the last word and flushing a little. Mary looked at her sharply. What had her friend meant to say, she wondered?

"That's good. Father says people should be individuals, not all alike as though they were eggs in a basket."

"And that's why he's made you go to school, I suppose."

"You could have come too. Still can." Mary eyed her friend curiously. The Walkers had always believed in school for girls as well as for boys, and no sooner had they settled on Bunker Hill Road in the little village five miles west of Oswego, New York, than they had started a school on their own property in a one-room building Alvah Walker had built himself. Mary's sisters had gone there, to be taught by their mother and father, who found time, somehow, in spite of farm chores. And now Mary, at the age of thirteen, was one of the handful of pupils. Nobody had "made" her go—she had wanted to go, and she still did.

Evvy Barnes's family had refused to let her attend.

"Book-learning for females doesn't make any sense," Evvy had reported proudly. "That's what Papa says. What good does it do? Mama teaches me cooking and sewing and all that. Why should I learn to read stuffy old books, or to figure things?"

"You have to have schooling if you want to do something with your life," Mary said, repeating what she had heard at home often enough. "Vesta taught until she was married, and Aurora does now."

"Is that what you want to do, teach school?" Evvy was scornful. The Barneses were newcomers in the neighborhood. When Mary had first told her father that Mr. Barnes wouldn't allow Evvy to attend the school, Alvah Walker had said, "Perhaps it's just as well. That girl doesn't look as though she'd take to learning handily, if you ask me." Now Mary wondered if perhaps some of Evvy's scorn might not be envy.

"No." Mary put her tongue between her teeth thoughtfully and tried to make up her mind. Should she tell Evvy what she had decided? Evvy didn't matter; what did matter was whether or not she wished to say out loud what was in her heart. It might make it more real to her. On the other hand it might, out in the open, sound ridiculous.

"I'm going to be a doctor," she said finally, lifting her chin.

"A doctor! You? A *lady* doctor! Oh Mary, you *are* crazy." Evvy giggled.

Mary looked at Evvy narrowly. Crazy—"your whole family is crazy"—was that what Evvy had started to say before when she finished with the word "different"? Well, it didn't matter what Evvy Barnes or Evvy's father or anyone thought about the Walkers. "*We* know we aren't crazy; we're just—advanced," Mary said to herself. "People are always jealous of those who are superior to them, Father said so."

"I must go home," Mary announced abruptly. She got up from her seat on the stone wall, brushed at her skirts, smoothed her hair with her palms, and left swiftly without a backward glance. Sometimes Evvy Barnes irritated her, in fact she often did, but with her older sisters all so busy, Mary was alone a great deal and needed a friend. Alvy, a year younger than she, didn't count. He was a boy.

Mary slowed her steps as soon as she was out of Evvy's sight. The wall where the girls had been sitting was between the Walkers' property and the Barnes's. It was a sad-looking wall, only partly built and in need of repair. No one seemed to have

time to fix it, and neither Mr. Walker nor Mr. Barnes could afford
to hire someone to come and do it for him. In Oswego there was
prosperity, and the people crowding into the community had to
be fed, so one would think the surrounding farms would be prosperous; but those living here in the village seemed to get little
benefit from the boom brought on by the dam that tamed the Oswego River and taught it to provide power, or from the Oswego
Canal that tied the Erie Canal in with Lake Ontario and made
Oswego an important harbor. Instead, the Walkers had as much
as they could do to feed themselves, and, partly because of the
hours spent in the little schoolhouse, everyone in the family
worked from dawn until dusk most of the time.

Mary was seldom depressed for long, and as she walked she
threw off the mood that Evvy had brought on her by being so critical. Tiny for her age, wiry, with wide curious eyes and long
brown curls that fell well below her shoulders, Mary usually
seemed to bounce as she walked.

"Mary, you have far too much energy for your own good," her
mother remarked frequently. This was, to a lesser degree, a trait
common to the whole family, and it was just as well, since life
seemed to demand so much of each of them.

Mary saw nothing wrong in the way they lived, and she extrav-
agantly admired her father and his views, no matter how "crazy"
Mr. Barnes and others thought them. Alvah Walker had traveled
before he married Mary's mother in Massachusetts—he'd been
all the way to New Orleans and back. He and his bride had
moved first to Syracuse, driving from Massachusetts in a wagon
over which he had, with some ingenuity, stretched a top so that
it was in effect a covered wagon. Mrs. Walker was fond of saying, "Oh, but I am a pioneer, you know. I crossed the desert of
New York in a covered wagon!"

Reading had always been important to both parents, and the
Walker girls and their brother read constantly as a matter of
course. Mary was especially interested in a shelf of medical books,
once bought by her father when he was worried about his own
health.

"Doctoring without knowledge is a terrible thing," Mr. Walker told his family. "Even those—" and he waved a hand at the volumes on medicine "—even those don't tell a man everything. Far from it. But they help him to understand what his body is all about, and what happens when this ill or that one strikes him, and then if he has true knowledge he can go about curing himself. Or, what is more important, of course, curing his fellow man. A man could do few things more valuable in this world than learn to treat the sick."

Mary's eyes had glowed at the words every time she heard them, but it was only recently that the thought had come to her: "Must it be a man? Why couldn't it be a woman? Wouldn't women especially rather talk to another woman? It must be terribly embarrassing to tell things to a man, sometimes."

At just the right moment, when questions were fluttering around in her head like chickens flapping aimlessly, she chanced on a book that the Walkers had just acquired. It was written by a missionary who, with her husband, had visited underprivileged countries. "The most important work here, of course," she wrote, "is that of my husband, who carries to these unfortunate people the Word of God, which will in time change their entire lives. But in my small way, as I try to cure their pains and illnesses, I am doing important work too. Oh, for more women—because women can walk more freely among these ignorant, frightened folk—to take care of the bodies while the men look after the souls."

That had been the final argument. It made Mary determined to follow the career she had daydreamed about and gave it form and meaning.

She was sure that her father would not only agree with her, but would encourage her, too, when she told him of her newest ambition, although surprisingly it took her nearly four years to get up her courage. Alvah Walker, perhaps because he had five daughters, had a special interest in women. There were a great many things going on in the world beyond Bunker Hill Road, and he liked to discuss all of the movements as news of them reached his ears. Spiritualism, Abolitionism, Temperance, for example, he explained to the best of his ability to his attentive family. But two of the "causes" caught his fancy in particular.

"That Convention," he said at supper, "over in Seneca Falls, that's for Women's Rights. Those women there claim that they have every bit as much right to do the things the menfolk do, and I don't know but I agree with them. Why shouldn't women vote, I ask you that? Vesta, you know more about what's going on in the world than that oaf Jacob Barnes next door, but he can vote and you can't."

"If I could vote, so could Emily Barnes," Mrs. Walker said with a smile.

"Well, then you would cancel her out, as I no doubt cancel Jacob," her husband retorted. "Thing is, in the long run as we get more education in this country, there'll be fewer idiots like those who went up into the hills and waited for the end of the world four years ago, and we'll get better government."

"And beside that," Aurora added, "if women had the vote, there would be eight people voting the way you wanted them to in this family!"

"I don't know about that," Alvah said. "I don't think Mary would vote the way I wanted her to. She'd probably do just the opposite, to be contrary."

"Contrary," it was agreed in the family, was the word for the youngest daughter. Mary didn't mind; sometimes she thought it offset the plainness of her first name. Contrary Mary—it had a ring to it. Frequently they didn't bother with the Mary but called out, "Contrary, where are you? Come here."

Her father was even more expansive when he talked about Amelia Bloomer of Seneca Falls, who had startled the whole world by appearing everywhere in the strangest costume—full Turkish trousers under a knee-length skirt.

"That woman is not only courageous, but she's on the right track," Mr. Walker declaimed. "She herself said that corsets are injurious to health, and she points out that all those layers of skirts weigh twelve pounds, sometimes even more. I agree with her fully that compressing your natural shape in steel torture instruments

just to conform to the lines of fashion is pure nonsense. So is sub-
mitting to the carrying of all that weight suspended from your
waist. I never want one of my girls to wear a corset ever, and I
wish Mrs. Bloomer all success."

Mary was thrilled at the idea of wearing trousers instead of a
skirt that swept the ground and was forever grimy and even
ragged at the hem. There was always a chance of tripping over it,
or of falling up or down stairs because of it. She wished she could
go to see Amelia Bloomer when she visited Oswego, but wasn't
able to get there. Even more, she wanted to go to see Amelia in
Seneca Falls, which wasn't far away in actual miles, but too dis-
tant for the Walker family to hitch up the horse and drive there
casually. To Mary, Seneca Falls was the center of the universe, a
kind of promised land. Amelia Jenks Bloomer and Elizabeth
Cady Stanton and the other women who made news because of
their fiery speeches at Seneca Falls and elsewhere were, in
Mary's young mind, goddesses.

Except for Cynthia, who had a genuine interest in clothes, the
Walker girls didn't pay much attention to fashion. Mary would
have said she cared nothing for what she called fripperies, but she
found herself reading newspaper accounts of Mrs. Bloomer's costumes, and she always saw with satisfaction that the lady put considerable emphasis on having pretty clothes, even if her costume
was unusual. Her skirts, short though they were, were always
decorated with bands of velvet, and she wore dashing colors and
diamond pins.

"She is not," Mary pointed out to Cynthia one day, as they
rested from their task of feeding the chickens, "trying to be a man,
or to look like one. She insists on being feminine. I think that's
important."

Cynthia yawned. "Why?" she asked.

"Because—well, people can't poke such fun of her if she has on
pretty clothes."

"Fun of her! Haven't you read about all the silly things they call
after her on the street—childish verses and all that? She must be
embarrassed to death."

"I'm sure she doesn't even hear them," Mary said stoutly. Amelia Bloomer had made a definite impression on Mary's mind, and now she couldn't see herself as a farmer's wife and mother of a growing brood of children, as Evvy Barnes pictured her own life. Mary felt lucky to be alive in a world that had a Women's Rights Convention in it, and women who dared to wear comfortable clothes.

Although she didn't realize it at the time, Mary Walker had been born in 1832 into an era of enthusiastic hotheads and fanatics. Every once in a while someone had a vision and started a new religion. A group of people were convinced that the end of the world was due on a certain day, and they had gone up into the hills to meet it, watched by a jeering public who felt uneasy about the outcome—supposing those Millerites were right? Other groups decided modern society wasn't what it should be, so they withdrew from the herd and began colonies of their own, living by their own rules. It was a restless world, and everyone in the Walker family agreed it would soon be a much better one—more free, more understanding.

Mary considered herself fortunate, too, in being able to read books on medicine, and she studied them in great bursts of industry, convinced that sooner or later she would be able to go to a medical school and learn more.

When at last she confided her ambition to her father, she found out that while Alvah Walker was sympathetic, he could not give her the money she needed.

"Mary, our biggest crop each year is rocks," Alvah told his youngest daughter regretfully. "And no one cares to buy those. In fact, everyone around here has a fine crop of his own. I couldn't send you to a medical school even if they'd take you, and they wouldn't. Guess you'll have to settle for a couple of terms at the Seminary, like your sisters. Then you'll have a profession, even if it's only teaching and not medicine. Teaching is a fine profession, you know that, and it will give you a chance to get out into the world and be somebody. That's the first big step anyway."

So Mary followed in her sisters' footsteps and went to Falley

Seminary, ten miles away. She studied as hard as she could, and two months after her nineteenth birthday she got a teaching position in a little town only five miles from Bunker Hill Road. She lived at home and saved almost all of her pay, for during all this time she was unwavering in her decision: the words she had spoken to Evvy Barnes nearly six years before somehow had to become a reality. "I'm going to be a doctor!" Nothing had changed.

Now that he realized Mary was prepared to be very contrary about her future, her father not only accepted her decision but he encouraged her in it, although he assured her again he couldn't help financially.

"There are two or three things that are favorable at the moment, Mary," he said, his gray eyes soft in his craggy face. Even Mary knew that she was, of course, pleasing him with her perseverance. He liked spirit and he liked spunk, and in flying in the face of tradition his youngest daughter was showing plenty of both. "For one thing, the medical profession, as I understand it, is in a bad way. There are all kinds of doctors in the world, with all sorts of ideas. Probably some of them are right, but they can't *all* be right. Depends on what school you go to, I guess, whether you think the best cure for everything is bloodletting, purging, one kind of drug or another, or spiritualism, or maybe a lot of other things we don't know about. Seems to me people are floundering around a good deal, trying to find ways to make us healthy. There are a lot more sick people than there are doctors, too, mostly because there are more people all the time. Doctors don't and can't keep up with them. That means that there are a lot of small colleges springing up everywhere that'll give degrees for going to classes there for a couple of years or even less. And with so many schools opening up, there's a kind of scramble for students who have the money to pay. It's inevitable that some of them would overlook their former scruples about what poor doctors females would make. There's that Elizabeth Blackwell—they accepted her over in Geneva. And there have been others since.

"So you go to it, Mary. I give you my blessing, as you know. My blessing but no cash, I'm sorry to say. I'm no better off now than I was when you first spoke to me about it. Worse, because I've upped the mortgage a bit. But a body can do what he wants to do, if he makes up his mind to it. And I know you've made yours up. You've been a determined little thing since you were born, small as you are, and I'm sorry for anyone who tries to stand in your way. You've got brains in that little head, and strength in that little body. If you can get some college to accept you, you go ahead and enroll, since you say you have enough money saved to see you through. Don't waste a minute of your time—learn everything they teach you, and some other things beside. Don't let anyone talk you into putting on steel corsets, or anything else that will be harmful to you. Sure you have enough money?"

"Enough to start, Father," Mary said staunchly. That was a truthful answer. She had enough to pay the tuition for the first two terms of the three she planned to be there. Board and room she had been told would cost between one and two dollars a week, and she thought she could just about manage that for the first winter. Incidental expenses she refused to worry about. Perhaps she could find some work in Syracuse that would help out her finances a little. Aunt Sally, her mother's sister, lived not far away. Perhaps she would know of something. And as soon as she had her degree and was established, her first fees would pay off the mortgage that worried her father so.

In December, 1853, just after her twenty-first birthday, Mary Walker entered the Syracuse Medical College, a school that was only two years old and had nine practicing physicians on the faculty. Contrary she might be, but determined she was too.

"I'll show them," she whispered to herself, riding along in the clattering railroad car that was taking her from Oswego to Syracuse. The Oswego and Syracuse Railroad had been in existence for five years, but it was Mary's first train ride, and the speed of the cars along the rails excited her—"faster than ten miles an hour," she had been told—as did the sight of the passengers sitting there taking this speed and motion for granted. And besides, think where she was going!

"I'll show them all!" she promised herself, clenching her fists tightly. Once, when she caught a glimpse of a small farm that looked very much like the one on Bunker Hill Road, she felt a wave of homesickness, but she lifted her chin, determined to hide the weakness from the fat man and his wife who sat opposite.

She knew they were interested in her, watching her thin eager face, the curls falling primly from under the bonnet, the full skirt arranged decorously over her tiny feet. She looked, she was sure, like any other young woman of her day. But she was different . . .

Mary grinned suddenly, throwing a merry glance at the woman opposite, who smiled back instinctively.

She imagines I just thought of my fiancé, Mary decided, and it made me smile. Instead, I was remembering that to Evvy Barnes, different and crazy were the same thing. And if that man and his silly wife knew just where I was going and why, they'd not hesitate to call me different either! What would they say if I remarked conversationally, "I am going to be a doctor?"

She pretended to be interested in the river along which the railroad tracks ran. Probably, she thought gleefully, the wife would swoon and the husband would turn purple and scowl at me. Well, I will sit here and look like a young lady journeying in this rattling railroad car to see her fiancé, and inside, where they can't see it, I will feel like a doctor!

2

the rocky road

To a girl who had never known a life other than that lived on a farm, Syracuse came as a surprise. She expected it to be large—there were more than fifteen thousand people living there, she had been told—but she was not prepared for the dirt that is a part of every city. The snow that had fallen in November was still on the ground when she arrived in the city the following month, but it was black or brown or gray snow, seemingly unrelated to the pure white blanket on the fields at home. The muddy roads were lined with irregular gray drifts, and the ruts grew deeper and deeper as wheels dug into dirt that thawed and froze and melted again.

Mary went first to the school, where she was given a list of four houses that had board and room. The man who seemed to run the untidy office at the College made it clear to her that because she was a woman she had presented an unusual problem. Dispirited, Mary asked to be allowed to leave in the office her box and the canvas bag that her mother had brought from Massachusetts in the covered wagon, and the man, his pale eyes cold and reluctant, agreed.

"There will be no one here after five o'clock," he said ungraciously. "We let the heat go off at three, to save fuel. It is too cold already to do any work, as you can see."

"I won't be long. Which way is—I can't read it," Mary said, pointing to the list.

"Bemis Street. It's to the left, one street over. Mrs. Shaw's house is on the corner. She has only one room free; you should hurry." He glanced toward the bag and box. "Perhaps you could take——"

"I won't be long. Thank you." Mary scuttled out of the dingy building. Her fingers were numb from carrying the luggage through the streets in the bitter cold, and she wanted to leave before he changed his mind and made her take her things with her.

Mrs. Shaw, when she opened the door and let Mary into the narrow hallway that smelled of cabbage and other foods cooked not too recently, was, Mary saw with relief, almost as short as she was herself. Very tall people often made her feel timid, and things were strange enough today anyway. Mrs. Shaw was, however, nearly as wide as she was tall. Looking into the little eyes set deep in creases of flesh, Mary felt her heart sink.

"Mr.—Mr. Johnson, at the Medical College, sent me. He said you had a room——"

"You going to work at that school?"

"I'm going to study there," Mary said proudly.

"Study to be a doctor? You? Land's sakes, people get crazier every day," Mrs. Shaw remarked. "Think anybody'd go to you, if you were a doctor?"

"If I were a good one, and I aim to be," Mary said. She wondered how many times she would be forced to defend herself. Somehow she had thought that here in Syracuse, where the College was, people wouldn't be so surprised at her. The College itself, or what she had seen of it, was a disappointment. She had expected several buildings set around a neat expanse of green— or, at this time of year, of white snow. But the school was

crammed into one building, an old residence badly in need of repair.

"We're building a fine new place, to be done soon," Mr. Johnson had told her, but she didn't believe him.

Mary tried to shake off the depression caused by the memory of
the building, the untidy office, and the unfriendly Mr. Johnson,
and she asked stiffly, "Do you have a room?"

"Well, yes. Top of the stairs, first on your right. Next door to the
bathroom, and it gets some sun in the morning. Good room."

Mrs. Shaw waved a plump hand at the stairway, and Mary ran
up quickly. She could understand why the fat little woman
wouldn't want to climb the narrow stairs often, and she was glad
enough of the chance to look at the room by herself. If it was at all
bearable, she would take it, she decided. It was close to the
school, and the figures that had been penciled in on the list Mr.
Johnson gave her showed it to be the cheapest of the lot. The food,
she felt sure, would be dreadful, but then, it might be bad almost
anywhere. She didn't eat much anyway, so food didn't matter.

The sun, she saw at once, might get into the room in the morning, but certainly not for long. The single window was set high
and it was narrow. It had been cut into the wall recently, Mary
suspected, and the room itself had no doubt once been part of a
hallway. There was just enough space for the iron cot, which was
pushed under the window; a chair; a table, which would serve as a
desk if it weren't too rickety; and a crooked chest of drawers.
Three wooden pegs were driven into the wall beside the door to
take the place, she supposed, of a clothes cupboard. The rug on
the floor was thin and badly worn, the cotton bedspread was
stained and its three-sided tears had been clumsily mended, and
the glass in the window was dirty. In the corner, on an old com-
mode, was a washbowl and a chipped pitcher half-full of rusty
water.

Mary looked around in despair, saw that dusk was creeping
through the dingy window, and made a quick decision. She had to
get her things from Mr. Johnson's office, and she was suddenly
aware of being more tired than she had ever been in her life. She

closed the door with a feeling of proprietorship, and ran lightly down the stairs.

"I'll take it," she said.

"That'll be one seventy-five, breakfast and supper."

"They—they said at the school a dollar and a half." Mary lifted her stubborn chin prepared to battle. To her surprise, Mrs. Shaw gave in immediately. Perhaps she had noticed the great weariness that had just swept over the little figure standing before her.

"That's right, I did tell 'em that. I may have to go up on it," she warned.

Mary nodded. "That'll give me time to look around for another place," she said pleasantly.

The small eyes glared at her. "In advance," said Mrs. Shaw.

Mary fished her purse out and carefully counted the money into the fat, grasping hand. Mary and her mother had made a sort of false bottom in the big handbag she carried, and most of her money was hidden there. The biggest part would be taken from its hiding place and paid into Mr. Johnson's fingers in the morning.

"Never let anyone know you have more than a dollar or two," her mother warned her. "Keep a little out where you don't mind it being seen, then no one will get ideas about trying to get your money away from you. Oh, Mary, I wish you weren't such a little thing. Somehow, I'd feel better about your going away if you were tall like the others."

Until she attended classes, Mary hadn't really given any thought to what it would be like to be the only girl in the school. She felt strange, of course, but it didn't bother her. If she found some subjects a little embarrassing, she didn't show it, she felt sure, but what really made it difficult for her was the way the others in class watched her face. After the first few days, during which her fellow students tried to tease her, they began to accept her. For one thing, she managed to act as though the teasing didn't touch her, and for another she convinced them all that she was perfectly serious about wanting to study medicine and to become a doctor.

The real reason why they seemed to decide to let her alone after a while was, although at first she didn't realize it, because of one of the students who took on the role of protector.

One day in January, right after a fresh snowfall, some of Mary's classmates began to throw snowballs, and Mary, watching out of the corner of her eye, knew that sooner or later one of them would manage to hit her before she could get out of range. She walked along sedately, pretending not to notice them, cringing slightly as she waited for the icy sphere to hit her face or head. Suddenly she felt someone move to a position right beside her, and a hand was slipped under her elbow.

"My name is Miller," he said, looking down at her. "I'd be glad to act as a screen for you, if you'll let me."

"Thank you." Mary looked up. Her new friend was very tall and thin, and she had noticed him right from the start. He seemed older than the others—might be twenty-eight or -nine, she thought—and there was something dashing and almost elegant about him. His clothes were better than the others, and he wore them with an air. The thing she had noticed first of all was that he always seemed to be the center of a group when they were not in class, and she had once or twice wistfully wished that she might make friends so easily. In class he was the one who usually answered the questions correctly and sometimes, she knew, he helped students who were having trouble with papers or examinations.

"My, you are a little thing, aren't you?" he said, smiling. "I know your last name is Walker, and I think your first is Mary. May I call you that, Miss Walker?"

Mary giggled nervously. "As long as it is my name," she said, "I think it would be all right."

"And I am Albert. There, we seem to have telescoped several months' courtesies into a minute or two. I have watched you, Miss Mary Walker, and first of all let me tell you that I have the greatest admiration for you."

"For me?" She had sometimes wondered what she would say if she suddenly found herself alone with a young man. Now it appeared that little was required of her, since Albert Miller was carrying the conversation easily.

"For you. The brave little woman who wishes to become a doctor. Before long I will find out all about you, including why you have such a burning ambition."

"He plans to see me again, to walk with me again," she thought dizzily, and looked around her just in time to notice that they were walking past Mrs. Shaw's.

"Oh! I live here!" she exclaimed. "Thank you for the protection, Mr.—Albert. Thank you very much."

She turned away and darted up the steps. In her room she looked into the small wavy mirror she had hung on the wall over her dresser. Her cheeks were pink, her eyes bright.

"It's the cold," she told herself severely. "It has nothing to do with Albert. Albert Miller, what a nice name!"

She continued to see Albert frequently, and he always paid the most flattering attention to her, but she was too busy to spend much time with him. Albert too was busy. The doctors who comprised the faculty of the school were practicing physicians themselves. They loaded the students with homework that often kept Mary at her books far into the night and also, under the pretense of providing laboratory and practical experience, made the students help whenever possible with their patients. Mary welcomed the difficult assignments and was especially pleased to be allowed to observe the doctors at work, but she had so many complaints from Mrs. Shaw about the number of candles she used that, annoyed at the constant carping, Mary bought a supplementary stock of her own.

"We don't have many luxuries at my house," she told Albert proudly, "but there's always oil for the lamps. My father doesn't think of reading as a luxury but a necessity, and we're all much too busy at home to read in the daylight hours."

She wished sometimes that she and Albert could have some time together, time to themselves. After weeks spent in the city, her country-girl's heart often longed for fields and forests, and when spring came she yearned to be away from the town, and dreamed of picnics and long walks by Onondaga Lake, which she had heard was very beautiful.

There was an elderly couple living at Mrs. Shaw's who moved Mary to compassion whenever she saw them. A few months before, their house had burned to the ground, with all their belongings. They had just enough money to pay for their board and room and stay out of the poorhouse, the threat of which nevertheless hung over them constantly. Still, sometimes they spoke at the table, and it was always to bring out some memory of their early life.

"We packed lunches and drove out to a special place on the lake," Mrs. Brown said, her sallow cheeks turning pink with re-membering. "Fried chicken, and fresh bread and butter, and——"

Mary didn't know where she could get fried chicken and fresh bread, certainly not from Mrs. Shaw, who seemed never to have heard of either, but sometimes she dreamed of being at the lake in a "special place" with Albert, living a moment that would some-day turn into a memory.

Sometimes Albert puzzled her. He was unfailingly polite and courteous to her, and he always seemed immensely glad to see her, snatching at a chance to walk home with her now and then, or to discuss some problem in their lessons, but Mary thought some-times he could have invented more opportunities to be with her. Once in a while, when it wasn't too cold or windy, they walked for an hour or so after they left the school. Albert liked to go down to the packet landing, opposite the Syracuse House, to look at the shops nearby and to observe the people who gathered around the landing waiting for the packet to tie up. He was much interested in the canal system.

"These ditches mean great things for the future," he assured Mary. "Commerce and trade and money in everyone's pocket. Money to pay doctors' bills even!"

Mary thought this walk something of a waste of time, and when she could she steered him toward the Jerry Rescue House.

"Why does it fascinate you so?" Albert asked, amused. "It's just like any other house around here."

"It's thrilling," Mary said stoutly. "When those men stood up for Jerry and rescued him, they were obeying their consciences, as men should do."

"They were breaking the law," Albert reminded her. "A law of the United States. They were helping an escaped slave elude his rightful owner."

"Slavery is wrong. A man shouldn't *belong* to anyone. Beside, lots of people helped the poor slaves along the Underground Railroad. These men took a greater risk than most, because the whole country knew about Jerry and everybody was watching."

"That was three years ago. Everyone's forgotten about it by now."

"I haven't."

"So I see."

"And I think *this* means great things for the future," she persisted. "We're Abolitionists, my family and I. Freeing slaves is more important than making money."

Albert took her arm and guided her away. After this argument Mary didn't see Albert for a while, except for glimpses in the classroom. She wondered if her championing of the men who had rescued the fugitive slave Jerry had disturbed him somehow, or her mention of Abolition. People were touchy about that, always violently for or violently against, it seemed. Perhaps he was just tired of her. She reminded herself that she was only a farm girl from a poor family, and that Albert came from well-to-do people in Cortland County who would no doubt look down their noses at her, so she was silly to expect too much attention from him. Beside, she reminded herself, she was too busy burying her nose in her books as soon as she got back to her room. And often she got up at four or five in the morning to return to her studies. There was no time for walking around and arguing with people.

Toward the end of the spring term, Dr. French, whom Mary had particularly liked and who had been the friendliest of the instructors toward their only woman student, called her into his laboratory.

"I need an assistant," he said brusquely, "for the summer. I have a practice in town, as you know, and I also wish to carry on my laboratory work, which is becoming important to me. But I don't wish to kill myself with work, and intend to have a little time for relaxation, so I need a helper who is willing to put up with me in order to learn something. I'd like it to be you, Miss Walker, if you'd be interested. I can pay only a little, but I think I could get the College to adjust your bill slightly next winter, since you could go on and assist me with classroom work. Also, my sister, Mrs. Eliza Winship, with whom I live, has an extra room and she would give you room and board free, if you accepted my proposition."

Mary floated home to Mrs. Shaw's on a cloud. She had wondered what employment she could find during the summer, and had dreaded the thought of going back to Bunker Hill Road to become an unpaid farm hand. Dr. French's offer was the answer to her prayer. She accepted at once, and prepared to move into Mrs. Winship's house as soon as school was over.

The only difficulty at the moment seemed to be Albert. She had assumed that he would stay in Syracuse for the summer, because most of the students at the College planned to. Some had jobs, others were continuing their studies with physicians in town, and two or three would be there under circumstances similar to Mary's own. But Albert, who had started walking home with her quite regularly again, had other plans.

"I like studying medicine, and I'll be back next term," he said breezily, "but I don't intend to swot away at it all summer. I mean to have some fun, for a change. And I can work with our family doctor, who will be only too glad to have me around whenever I feel like spending some time with him. Take the summer off, Mary. You'll be more ready to get down to work in the autumn, you know."

Mary thought he must suspect that she needed the money, but her pride forbade her to remind him of it, so she let it go. She tried to forget her disappointment, and she found that she was looking forward eagerly to escaping from her shabby, cramped little room and from Mrs. Shaw's indifferent meals.

On the day after the term's end, Dr. French sent a man to Mrs. Shaw's to help her with the bags. Mary followed him eagerly through the streets. In the warm spring air, and under the golden influence of the sun, Syracuse no longer looked crowded and dirty to her. The canal was a long mirror, when they crossed it, and she thought the trees, fully leafed, stately and beautiful. As they walked on into a neighborhood of fine homes, Mary's heart was singing. Things were indeed taking a turn for the better; the dreary weeks of winter, the cold, unpleasant little room, the taciturn, watchful lodgers, the sly jibes of her classmates—they were all forgotten. She was starting a new life.

Mary had expected Mrs. Winship to be standing on the front porch to greet her and to welcome her into the Winship home, but the man who had silently carried her bag and box through the streets jerked his head to indicate she should follow him, and led her around by the carriage house to the back door of the imposing white frame home. She followed him through the kitchen, where a cook and maid looked at her curiously, and up narrow stairs to a room on the third floor that was, she realized instantly, one of the servants' rooms. There the man deposited her things and, still without a word, left her.

Drearily she unpacked. This was hardly what she had expected. Gradually, though, her spirits rose. The room, small as it was, was larger than the one she had been living in, and it was spotless. It even had rose-sprigged curtains at the window. Mary inspected them and saw that they were clumsily stitched. Some maid, she thought, had tried to make the room into a home for herself. Well, they did help. So did the scene from the window which instead of providing a view of an alleyway filled with rubbish and debris, looked into the green branches of a maple tree. Below there was velvety grass, and along the graveled drive there were beds of pansies and others of petunias. As for her being in this room as though she were a servant instead of a colleague, when Dr. French came home he would no doubt discover there had been a mistake.

There was no mistake. Mary found she was to eat in the kitchen with the cook, the maids, and the dour man who had brought her to the house. She didn't meet Mrs. Winship, who was a widow, for nearly a week, and then found herself being eyed sharply. For the first time she realized that possibly her unwilling hostess had thought this female student might try, perhaps, to take from her her unmarried brother and so disrupt the even tenor of her life. There was little enough danger of that, Mary thought, as she trotted back and forth between the house and Dr. French's laboratory. As a doctor, he was warm and human, interested in his work, trying constantly to learn and grow. But socially she thought him frivolous, always hurrying off to a party of some kind, and he and his sister entertained a great deal. The two pieces didn't fit, Mary felt. A dedicated doctor had no time to be social. It's that woman's doing, she thought resentfully, watching Mrs. Winship's tall and elegant figure, dressed in the latest fashion and always tightly corseted—she's the one who wants to be social.

Just the same, Mary enjoyed herself. She was here to work and learn, and work and learn she would. As for the pretty clothes, the plumed hats, the glittering jewels, the hourglass figure—she tried to put them all out of her mind. The time would come when useless women like Mrs. Winship would be laughed at, she was sure of it.

Actually, Mary was more alone than she had ever been in her life, even at Mrs. Shaw's. She knew in her heart she should have troubled to make friends with the cook and the maids with whom she ate. If she had taken the initiative and made a pretense of being interested in their conversation, she could at least have spent some of her time sitting in the comfortable, scrubbed kitchen, and would have had, occasionally, someone to talk to. But she made no effort to join their gossipy discussions, which she considered beneath her notice, and the others in time talked as though she wasn't even at the table.

Dr. French had told her she might use his medical books whenever she liked, and much of the time she spent in her room, poring over them, delighted to have an opportunity to read volumes that not even the College library had been able to provide. The rest of her waking hours were spent either in Dr. French's office or in his laboratory, and once in a while he invited her to accompany him on his rare house calls. For a few weeks they were both very busy as cholera invaded the city, following, she was told, the rivers and canals, but because of Dr. French and the other doctors the threatened epidemic didn't develop. Still, there were enough cases to take up much of their time, and a few deaths.

She was glad when the summer was over. Just before the winter term began she took time to look around the town and found another room. This one was less dismal and much less dingy than the one at Mrs. Shaw's, and she was more comfortable there. There were other students in the house, all men, of course, but Mary resisted their friendly advances and froze out attempts at familiarity. Their loud talk and laughter annoyed her. Suddenly she wanted to be through with college; she wanted to be out in the world practicing medicine. She would earn money and be self-supporting, she would help out her family, she would live well, she would have a long list of patients who would look up to her and be dependent on her, and she would gain fame as a lady doctor who was every bit as good at the job as any man. And furthermore, she had decided, as she watched Mrs. Winship sweep in and out of the house in her frilled silks and her pinched-in waist, that she would show the world how women should dress.

Her head was full of plans and dreams, but in spite of them she managed to concentrate on her studies. Dr. French allowed her to work with him through the winter, paying her enough for her board and room. He didn't suggest a return to his sister's house, she noticed, but she was pleased that he didn't. Albert often stopped in at the laboratory to take her for a walk. Twice he got tickets to the Musical Institute Concerts at City Hall, but Mary had no ear for music, and after he discovered the concerts bored her, he didn't ask her again.

At last it was June and she was officially awarded her medical degree, graduating as the only woman in her class. The whole thing, as she looked back on it, seemed to have been accomplished with breakneck speed. Now the end had come, and when she looked at the list of courses she had taken, she was proud. She had, it was true, spent not too much time on any single subject, but she had learned something of all of them. She had spent three terms in the Syracuse Medical College, and had a certificate to prove it.

She was proud of Albert too. She had seen more and more of him lately, and she had even helped him with the speech he gave to the alumni at graduation. That he had been selected by the faculty to give the speech she thought a tremendous honor.

"They should have asked you to do it, little one," he told her teasingly.

"Me?"

"Yes, you. I suspect somewhere in that small frame lies the soul of a great orator. And besides, think how startled the alumni would be, poor souls, to have a fellow alumnus—alumna, pardon me—in skirts tell them how ignorant they are."

"Oh, Albert! Are you going to tell them that?"

He didn't; he told the upturned faces what they wanted to hear —how wonderful they were—and his speech was a success. Mary sat in her place and her heart swelled with pride. Albert was still the dashing figure she had first thought him and, most amazingly, he had singled her out for attention. It was enough to make her head swim—and it did.

And—on top of everything else—there was in her hand that precious piece of paper that proclaimed to the whole world that Mary Edwards Walker was a doctor of medicine!

3

the lady doctor

It was her father's idea that she practice her profession in Ohio.

"Your Aunt Harriet is a widow and childless" he said. "She has a large home and rattles about in it. She needs an interest, she has always wished to know my children better, and you must establish yourself in a much larger community than this one. In Oswego you would be too near to your home and your family—it would not do. I've already written to my sister about this and she is much pleased with the thought of having you with her."

Columbus, Ohio, seemed a long way from home to Mary. It was also a long way from Rome, New York, where Albert was setting up his own practice. But the matter had been taken out of her hands and for once Mary didn't dig in her heels obstinately and insist on having her own way.

"So Oswego is not good enough for you," Evvy Barnes, now Evvy Blake, remarked scornfully. "Not even New York State. No, you must go to Ohio!"

Mary looked at Evvy and wondered why they even saw each
other now. Evvy carped at Mary's achievements, her learning, her
medical degree, everything she did. And as far as Mary was concerned, Evvy counted for nothing. She had married Joseph Blake,
and she lived on her parents' farm, for her mother had died and
her father was now a semi-invalid. Evvy was just what she said she
would be—a farmer's wife and nothing more.

"Columbus is a large town, with nearly twenty thousand people," Mary told her. "And my Aunt Harriet expects me."

The idea did have appeal. Aunt Harriet, whom she remembered dimly as a sweet-faced, silent little woman, would at least
be someone to talk to, and more important, she would be able to
introduce her to patients, just at first. After a while, of course, the
waiting room would be filled, but even Mary could see that to
begin with, it would be useful to have a friend at hand who knew
everyone.

Aunt Harriet, she discovered, had changed. In some ways she
was much like Mary herself—short, wiry, determined. And it was
plain enough before Mary had lived there very long that she was
more interested in providing herself with a companion than in
launching Mary as a physician.

"Take some time to know folks around here," she advised. "My
garden is in bad shape, and between us we can restore it to the
order my late husband demanded of it." It wasn't until later that
Mary realized that the two sentences were definitely linked in her
aunt's mind. Aunt Harriet wanted help with her garden; the advice to Mary to get to know people in Columbus was given to en-
sure that help.

Before Mary had been in the house too long, her aunt said, "You
and I can take turn-and-turn-about on the cooking, Mary. My late
husband disliked cooks, and I am out of the habit of one, having
Sarah come in for cleaning only."

"I can't cook," Mary retorted firmly. "Mother declared me un-
teachable in that direction. It's too bad I'm the one here instead of
Vesta or Cynthia. They're quite at home in the kitchen. Aurora
too, of course, and Luna."

On another occasion her aunt looked with distaste at Mary's

second-best dress and said, "We must get you some new clothes, child. What will my friends think, when I come to introduce you to them? And even here, in the house—supposing one of them should come to call and find you like that? Unless, of course, you plan to help me in the garden."

"I'm sorry, Aunt Harriet, but I am not interested in new clothes. Your friends must take me as I am—a penniless young doctor. At least, until my practice grows into something profitable. Also, I doubt I will have much chance to help with your garden. A physician works long hours, and there will be many calls to make on patients in and around the town, and of course one must continue to study."

Before long she realized that Aunt Harriet not only didn't want to help her establish a practice, but she was slightly ashamed of her niece's peculiar ambition. Mary's mouth set in the obstinate line her family knew so well, the one that had inevitably started her sisters to chanting, *Mary, Mary, quite contrary.* She had hoped to be offered a room in Aunt Harriet's house for her office, but seeing that it would not be suggested, Mary began to walk around the unfamiliar city looking for a suitable place. The second week of her stay in Ohio she found one, not far from Neil Avenue, and moved her books and her small medical kit into it.

The weather was unkind to a girl trudging along the streets. It rained fitfully all the time, and the winds blew, flapping her wet skirts about. Each night Mary sponged off the hem of her second-best dress and tried to make it look presentable for the next day, when she knew she must go through the whole process again.

"It is ridiculous," she muttered to herself, closing her ears to Aunt Harriet's fretful monologues, which consisted mostly of references to her late husband. Mary thought it strange her uncle was never called by name. "How did Aunt Harriet address him when he was here?" she wondered. Then she turned back to cleaning her skirt. "Why should women drag the dirt of the streets about with them?" she thought angrily. A picture of Mrs. Amelia Bloomer flashed into her mind. If she dressed in the sensible costume worn with such dash by Mrs. Bloomer, she wouldn't be

spending valuable time each evening trying to make her long
skirts wearable for another day.

Mary thrust her tongue between her teeth as she did when she
was thinking. "Why not?" she asked herself. "I am, as Aunt Harriet insists, going to meet considerable resistance here anyway,
because I am a female. Why not show these people that females
can not only practice medicine, but they can think for themselves,
they can break the bonds of silly fashion and be comfortable?"

"Ah, I see you have at last decided to take my advice," Aunt
Harriet said the next day. Mary had bought a length of service-
able material and was sewing busily. She was not much of a seam-
stress, and of course there was no pattern or model for what she
was making, but she would do the best she could. She smiled at
her aunt and said nothing. Aunt Harriet would be surprised at the
result, and probably not too pleased.

Aunt Harriet's reaction to Mary's costume, when she first saw it,
was even more violent than Mary had anticipated.

"Mary Walker, you will not go out in the streets in that—
that——" she gasped. Mary looked down at herself complacently.
She had managed to stitch up some fairly presentable Turkish-
type trousers, over which she wore a long tunic made by shorten-
ing an old lightweight coat. She thought the result was most successful.

"You will become used to it, Aunt Harriet," she said kindly.
"The whole world is startled at first. But Mrs. Bloomer and her
followers are showing the rest of us the way."

"I don't know about that Amelia Bloomer," Aunt Harriet said
faintly. "I think she's moonstruck. But I did read in the paper the
other day that most of her 'followers,' as you call them, have given
up those—those unspeakable *things,* and are wearing skirts just
like normal women again. My poor brother, what would he say if
he could see you like that?"

"Father would be delighted," Mary told her serenely. "He's always been against long, dragging skirts and tight, cruel corsets."

For some reason her mind veered to Evvy Barnes—Evvy
Blake. Always when she did something that pleased her, Mary

found that she wished to have Evvy know about it at once. Was it because Evvy was usually so smug, so sure she was right? Or because she had said more than once—or at least, had implied—that Mary, along with the rest of the Walker family, was crazy? Or was it because Evvy's life was so humdrum and dull, fitting always into a predictable pattern, especially when contrasted with her own, which contained so many elements of novelty and excitement?

Turning before the mirror, Mary smiled complacently. She must, after she had worn her new bloomers a few times, write to Evvy—even send her a sketch. That would give the poor girl something to think about! Her mind flitted back again to her father. He, too, must have a sketch, she decided.

"Yes," she added now to Aunt Harriet, "Father will be pleased. He likes us to think for ourselves. And he has lectured us all for so long about the idiotic clothes women wear."

Aunt Harriet looked as though she didn't believe a word of it. "Do you think you will get anyone to visit you in your office, Mary Walker, if you look like a freak? Throw those bloomer things away, I implore you."

Mary pivoted once more, craning her neck to see herself in the glass above the sideboard.

"No indeed, Aunt. I am happy with this costume. It is healthy and practical and—I think, at least—most becoming. Sooner or later I expect we will change from these full bloomers to trousers, like the men."

Aunt Harriet uttered one last squeak of dismay and hurried upstairs. She stayed in her room the rest of the day, and when Mary returned, after having triumphantly seen her first three patients, her aunt refused to speak to her, but ate supper silently, her eyes stubbornly on her plate. Mary talked about her patients anyway. Two of them were the result of an accident that had taken place almost in front of her office, and the other had been the owner of the house where the office was located. She described the accident in detail to her aunt, the wheel rolling from the carriage, the horse frightened and rearing, the bystanders screaming. There had been cuts and bruises and even a broken wrist to set! It didn't occur to Mary that for the first time in that house she was doing the talking, or that for the first time she had something to talk about. She was thrilled and excited and keyed up. *Now* she was a practicing physician.

Aunt Harriet, in the following weeks, changed even more. She never again became as friendly with her niece as she had been at first, and she said little or nothing about either the medical practice or the costume. It was true that Mary was stared at and laughed at on the street, and she knew that some people shied away from her office because of her clothes. Her landlord, Mr. Libby, told her that, grinning a crooked grin and shaking his head.

"People want to know do you talk and act like a woman or a freak," he stated. "I say you're no different than the rest of 'em, except for the funny clothes. You'd think some of 'em would come here just to get a good look at you up close, wouldn't you? 'Spect that's why you dress this way anyhow, isn't it—to make 'em curious enough to visit you?"

"Of course not," Mary snapped. "I dress this way because it's both healthful and convenient. Women don't seem to realize that the current styles are killing them. What woman can do all that is required of her in the way of physical or mental labor if she's carrying around from twelve to fifteen pounds of clothing, perhaps an eighth of her own weight, or maybe even more?"

Mr. Libby shrugged. "It could be a good stunt, if you worked it right. People are curious; they love traveling shows and all that. But I suppose once they see you, they don't care to have you doctor them. Those as do, do they pay you?"

Mary made a face. "Some of them seem to think they won't have to pay me as much as they would a man," she admitted. "But I tell them my education is as good as a man's, and that it cost me just as much. Beside, the obstacles I was faced with were greater. I ought to charge more, not less."

Mr. Libby shrugged again. "Maybe your business will pick up," he said vaguely, and Mary, looking after him, knew he was interested in his rent rather than her problems. Besides, he had never even offered to pay for the powders she had given him for his headaches.

Her practice did "pick up," but not much. Mary blamed the town, the location of her office—everything but her sex and her unusual costume. In fact, she even made good her words to her aunt and made for herself a pair of men's trousers. She lacked the courage to wear them, though, telling herself that she must first accustom this narrow-minded city to the bloomers.

She was, after a few months, thoroughly discouraged. Aunt Harriet not only did nothing to help her with her practice, but she had become a bitter and complaining woman, lashing out at her niece at every opportunity. And there weren't enough patients to give Mary sufficient money to support herself. Just as she was wondering what to do, she received a most astonishing letter from Albert Miller.

"I read between the lines, little one," the letter said. "You pretend you are satisfied that patients will fill your office shortly, but I'm sure you know that they won't. You are trying to do the impossible all by yourself. I have been told that an impossible weight can sometimes be moved if there is more than one shoulder applied to the wheel. I have a suggestion, therefore, and I want you to think about it carefully. Do you not suppose a lady doctor would prove more acceptable in an office in which there were two doctors, one male and one female? Would that not give the lady an air of respectability and even responsibility? Especially if the lady doctor was wife to the gentleman doctor, and they functioned together as a team?

"That is my suggestion. Why not shake the dust of Ohio from your skirts and join me in Rome—as my wife and as my medical partner? My business is improving rapidly, and I have every belief that a common medical practice would be of benefit to us both."

It was hardly a love letter, Mary thought at first. Then she saw that Albert was shrewdly making the approach in the direction where he knew she would be most susceptible. He was, in effect, offering to bail her out of an awkward situation. And why should

she expect—or even want—a love letter? Things should be busi-
nesslike between them. She had been a silly girl before, when she
had looked at Albert and thought him dashing and romantic. The
months in Columbus had made great changes in her. Her practice,
her clothes, her ideals, had become all-important. And Albert was
going to help her with them all.

She didn't wait long before she replied, and of course she told
him yes. At first she thought to correct him, saying she would have
no need to shake the dust of Ohio from her skirts because she had
abandoned those dust-collecting garments, but she thought better
of it. I will surprise him, she decided.

Back on Bunker Hill Road, where the wedding was to take
place, she surprised him indeed. Albert drove up to the Walker
farm, leaped from his hired carriage, and was met by his bride.
Mary had decided to use this occasion for the first wearing of her
new trousers, and her wedding costume consisted of a dress coat
over the unorthodox pants. Even her father had been startled
when he saw her outfit, and her mother had turned pale.

"Mary, dear," Mrs. Walker said, "of course I know how you feel,
how we all feel, about the fashions of the day. But—for your wedding? Surely that is one time when a girl wishes to look her pretti-
est. What will Dr. Miller say?"

"Albert expects the unusual from me," Mary replied. "You
know how quickly he accepted me as a medical student and a doctor. He believes in what I believe in—it's as simple as that."

Her mother, watching when Albert arrived, must have had
some doubts. He stopped short and stared, his face turning first
white and then red. Mary tripped forward, holding out her hand.
It did not seem to her an odd greeting to the man she would
within an hour be married to, any more than her costume seemed
to her incongruous with her carefully curled hair.

"I don't want anyone to forget I'm a woman," she had explained
to Aurora and Vesta, who had traveled to the farm early to help
dress the bride, and who had gaped in amazement when they saw
her. "I am not trying to be a man, and you two know this better
than anyone. I am trying to be a woman who dresses sensibly. You

remember what pains Amelia Bloomer always takes with her appearance, determined to look dainty and feminine in her sensible clothes."

She used the present tense firmly, although there had been rumors that Mrs. Bloomer had gone back to skirts, or at least intended to, as so many of her disciples had already done. Amelia Bloomer, of all people!

Vesta, like her mother, tried to argue Mary into a different costume, but Aurora took it calmly. Aurora was seven years older than Mary, and had always been the closest to her. She was now Mrs. Lyman Coats, and in her own way as self-reliant and independent as Contrary Mary herself. Instead of taking up causes and good works, Aurora had thrown all of her energy into her marriage and motherhood, but she hadn't let her mind stagnate. She read widely, gave speeches to local groups on all sorts of subjects, and was appealed to at once by anyone in trouble. Aurora was proud of Mary's achievements, but she was not envious. It was part of Aurora's live-and-let-live policy that made her smile encouragement at her sister's odd bridal outfit.

"Be quiet, Vesta," she said gently. "Mary is the bride, after all, and has the right to dress as she wishes."

"I think," snorted Vesta, "that for once she is carrying contrariness to an extreme," and Luna and Cynthia, arriving later, agreed with her.

At the last moment, Mary sent Cynthia to Evvy's, to invite her to the wedding. Mrs. Walker had reported earlier that Evvy had expressed surprise that Mary was getting married.

"I'm sure I don't know why, dear," Mary's mother had added. "Perhaps she believes that education is a deterrent to marriage."

Mary giggled. "We used to argue about that very thing. I was forever saying I would be much too busy and famous to bother with marriage. And she, I think, took that to mean that I was resigning myself to the fact that no one would ask me to be his wife. When I used to talk about one day going to medical school, she always told me that I would scare men off, by knowing so much.

Scare men like her Joseph, that is certain! When he merely looks
at me his face turns as red as a beet."

Mary thought of Albert—tall, thin, so distinguished looking—
and mentally compared him to Joseph Blake. It was then that she
decided Evvy should see the man who had asked Mary Walker to
be his wife.

"Cynthia, run down the road and ask Evvy to come to the ceremony," she said. "Well, she *is* my oldest friend. She should be
here."

Cynthia shrugged and went away.

"She can't come," Cynthia reported on her return. "That is, she
says she can't. I think she won't. But she did ask if she could lend
you a handkerchief, Mary, for the 'something borrowed,' you
know. Here it is. I think if she knew it was going to be put into a
pant's pocket instead of down a bodice, she'd refuse to let you
have it. *I* would."

Mary took the handkerchief. She was oddly moved.

"Will you give it back to her later, Cynthia? And tell her I thank
her."

"And describe your wedding dress? Gladly," Cynthia snapped.

"I'll give the handkerchief back to Evvy," Aurora said quickly.
"You look lovely, little Contrary."

"Lovely! That poor man downstairs. My heart goes out to him!"
Cynthia exclaimed.

After his first start of astonishment, Albert recovered quickly.
Mrs. Walker, watching him carefully, noticed that his eyes flicked
over Mary's petite figure again and again, and she suspected that
although he had been truly startled at the sight of his bride, he
was carrying it off well. At the ceremony he didn't even blink—or
perhaps, his to-be mother-in-law thought, he hadn't even noticed
—when the familiar promise of the bride to obey her husband was
left out of the ceremony. Mary had thought about that a great
deal, and she had searched out a minister to perform the ceremony who would permit the change.

"What woman would wish to 'serve' or 'obey' a man? Ridiculous," she had said.

Albert and Mary drove away in a hired carriage. If Albert had
cringed at the thought of traveling with a wife in such odd regalia,
he gave no sign of it, and pretended not to see the stares and leers
that followed them whenever they got out of the carriage. He had
planned to stay a few days at a place he knew on Oneida Lake,
about two-thirds of the way to Rome, but Mary said she was much
too impatient to get back to work, and reminded him that his patients were depending on him. He gave in quickly. Perhaps, she
thought, Albert wasn't quite ready to escort around a fashionable
resort a lady whose costumes would be the center of all eyes.

For the most part she enjoyed the brief trip from Oswego to
Rome, her small face alight with interest at everything they saw.
She was full of optimism about the future; in Rome, with Albert's
help, she would have a flourishing practice, and that was what she
had dreamed of for so long.

Albert got still another surprise when Mary told him firmly that
she had no intention of using his name.

"I will never be called Dr. Mary Miller, or Mrs. Albert Miller,
which is worse. Why women wish to have themselves and their
identities swallowed up utterly, by giving up *both* Christian and
last names, I can't imagine!" she said. "Lucy Stone is absolutely
right. Why should I become Mrs. Anybody? I suppose the day will
come when men, to make their wives agree to being branded with
Missis, will adopt the term Misterer, or some such title, to en-
lighten the world as to their married condition. If you like, Albert,
I can make it Dr. Mary E. M. Walker. If anyone should ask, I'll tell
them the M. is for Miller. There, that should satisfy you," she said,
and it was obvious that she considered the subject closed.

Albert, bewildered, said nothing. Mary had long ago told him
her sisters called her "Contrary Mary" and he was undoubtedly
beginning to believe it was with cause. He glanced at the trousers
and then at the carefully arranged curls, and smiled. Soon enough
this fancy would pass, he thought. As Mrs. Miller—and of course
she would come to it presently, it must be a shock for a girl to
change her name, to become suddenly someone else. As Mrs.
Miller she would delight in the pretty new frocks he would buy for

her, and she would be a charming exception in the world of male doctors. Then, after the children came, she probably would forget all about being a doctor, but would of course always help him with his papers and reports. Her brain was to be valued, Albert knew that well, and her education could be put to good use.

Mary was unaware of his thoughts, which were far different from her own. Hers were fixed on her medical career, although she had promised herself that she would be a good wife to him. She would assist Albert not only in his profession, but she would run his house properly, seeing to it that the housekeeper met her own high standards at all times. Mary simply assumed that Albert's housekeeper would stay on, since she herself would be much too busy doctoring the sick to do any of the actual work of cleaning and cooking.

Mrs. Smythe, the housekeeper, took one look at her new mistress' costume, and gave notice.

"Mrs. Smythe, please—please wait a moment before you decide anything," Albert begged. "Dr. Walker—I mean Mrs. Miller—I mean my wife has told me that she wishes you to remain with us."

"Indeed I do," Mary agreed, with her most charming smile. "I will be in the office as much as my husband, you see, Mrs. Smythe. Dr. Miller has told me how efficient you are, and I earnestly wish you to go on taking care of him, and of me too. I won't bother you, I promise you that."

Finally, Albert carried Mrs. Smythe off to another room, where he talked to her alone. Mary, prowling around her new home, wondered if he was offering the woman more money. She hoped not. She had a feeling that while most women were underpaid in their jobs, those who did housework were given too much money, because what skill and training did that sort of an occupation demand anyway? It hadn't occurred to her that Mrs. Smythe's sudden decision to leave had anything to do with her own trousers. She had, in fact, forgotten all about them.

Mrs. Smythe was persuaded to stay, and the household settled down into a routine that was, to Mary at least, satisfactory. She soon discovered that the housekeeper didn't like interference, so as long as the work was done properly, Mary stayed away from her. She liked to think her hand was on the helm, however. "I am running a tight ship," she wrote to Aurora, "with Mrs. Smythe, who used to be Albert's housekeeper, as my cook and maid."

Mary was happy. Patients did come to her. At first Albert referred some of his—usually women and children—to his wife, and they were content to accept his recommendation, but they did continue to look askance at her costume. So did Albert. Sometimes he begged her to wear a dress to a concert or reception, but she refused, and more and more he went out without her, or turned down invitations for them both. Mary didn't mind. As long as she had her work, she was happy.

It came as a shock, after she had been married for three years, to discover that Albert was not. His long silences and occasional grumbling she believed to be part of his character, just as constant chattering and an inability to sit still for two minutes at a time was part of hers.

She managed to find a great deal to occupy herself, although it was several weeks before she realized that the women of Rome were not to be a part of her life. A few had called on the new bride, and Mary, earnestly trying to do the right thing, had returned the calls dutifully, but there it had ended. When she and Albert met his old women friends on the street, Albert received cordial smiles but Mary got only frozen nods.

Jealous, Mary decided. Jealous because Albert chose an intelligent and educated woman for his wife, instead of a social butterfly. But before long she admitted to herself that there was more to it than that. Her profession and her dress counted against her, and of course she had no intention of changing either one.

"They're silly, aimless females," Mary wrote to Aurora. "And even if I did like them, I wouldn't have time for them."

She filled in her life with her preoccupation with dress reform, and spent more and more time at her writing desk, dashing off letters to newspapers and to kindred souls who also addressed long, vehement letters to editors on the subjects dearest to Mary's heart. She was reading one of her own letters, printed, to her delight, in a New York City paper, to Albert at the dinner table one night, emphasizing, with waves of her fork, the important points she had made.

"They should not have shortened it," she said regretfully, as she came to the end. "If a newspaper editor deems a letter worthy of publication, he should give the writer the honor of printing it all. The most important sentence here, the one in the third paragraph, should have appeared in its entirety. It has lost some of its significance. But still, the letter, even mutilated as it is, makes its point, don't you think so? I must pick up an extra copy and send it to Father. He is always so interested in my little successes. And although it is the fashion nowadays to use a *nom de plume*, I believe the next time I shall be bold and sign my own name. People have a right to know who the individuals are who are working so hard to right the world for them."

"Just so long," remarked Albert quietly, "as you don't use *my* name."

"But Albert!" Mary was genuinely astonished. "You used to be at me all the time about being Mrs. Miller. Have you changed your mind about that?"

"I have changed my mind about many things." He raised his eyes, bright behind his spectacles, to Mary's. "And I have *not* changed my mind about many others. For example, I cannot yet bring myself to enjoy having a wife who wears bloomers or trousers. Whenever we walk down the street together, and you may have noticed that we do that as seldom as possible these days, I am both embarrassed and ashamed. I find it most upsetting to have people stare at my companion as though she were a side show of some kind, and I find it increasingly difficult to try to pretend that I don't notice the sneers and leers that you occasion on the faces of those who used to be my friends. Furthermore, I suspect I am losing patients because my partner in practice is a woman who persists in being a freak."

"But Albert!" Mary cried again. "Your practice is growing. The waiting room is becoming fuller all the time."

"Yes," he agreed dryly, "I believe that is so. But I am equally sure that many of those who sit for a while in our waiting room, and who spend a few minutes having minor aches and pains discussed, are there to see the odd little Dr. Walker, who should be known as Mrs. Miller, since a large percentage of them never become regular patients or for that matter return at all."

"That isn't true," Mary denied hotly. "I have stayed in the office well after the regular hours, time and time again."

"Because you can't bear to let a patient get away from you," Albert said unkindly. "You wish to prove how learned you are, and you launch into entire lectures, time and again. I have heard that from a number of people. I will say that you do not allow your ridiculous activities to interfere with your practice—not much, anyway. I grant you that. But you are and always have been more interested in the practice than in your home and your husband, and I am heartily sick of it. In the morning I am going away for a few days. I may come back and I may not. But I assure you that I do not like the way things are done around here, and it is, unless you mend your ways, to be clearly understood that other arrangements probably will be made. I promise you that."

Mary watched him drive away from the house the next morning. She felt a little frightened. She was fond of Albert, genuinely fond, and she didn't want him to stay away permanently. Before long her good spirits returned. He would be back in a day or two, she told herself, and she was right. Albert returned, perhaps even more taciturn than before and with no explanation as to where he had been, but he was back.

The scene was repeated many times, occurring at more frequent intervals and resulting in longer separations, but Mary appeared not to notice. She was busier than ever, as dress reform became increasingly important to her and began to attract attention around the country. Both in writing and in speaking, she started to use glib phrases about "freedom of motion" and "equal distribution of clothing," pointing out over and over that the weight of a heavy skirt together with that of several petticoats was borne by the waist alone, and the waist, furthermore, being pinched in cruelly by corsets, already had more punishment than it could bear.

Cheerfully she developed what she considered the perfect dress for women. "Of only three pieces," she wrote, "which makes it both easy to wear and easy and economical to fashion. First there is the linen undergarment, with a high neck, a loose waist, and long drawers that fold neatly over the ankles. The stockings are pulled up over these folds, which means that the ankles are always warm, and also that no garters are needed. Over this one should wear bloomers or trousers, according to one's preference, which may be buttoned to the undergarment or held up in the usual manner by suspenders. Lastly comes the dress, which consists actually of a skirt and waist in one piece, rising neatly to the chin and falling gracefully to the knees. With the undersuit, the trousers, and the frock, a woman is well-dressed and comfortable at all times."

Sometimes she outdid herself. Once, in a burst of inspiration, she described the many costumes required by fashion for one day's wardrobe—if, of course, one was foolish enough to dress for the morning, change to another costume for the midday meal, put on an afternoon frock, and don more formal attire for the evening. "Just think," she wrote happily, "of the poor creature who not only dons and doffs several costumes a day, but must plan these many outfits, deciding what is suitable for which occasion, shop for the materials, stand while they are being fitted, choose ribbons and brooches and bonnets to match. How much more fortunate her sister who adopts the reform dress, thus saving money, time, and, above all, energy."

When word reached her that Mrs. Bloomer had actually forsaken her bloomers and now wore hoops, Mary was enraged. "Hoops are lightweight, they are nothing like the heavy dragging skirts of yesterday," Mrs. Bloomer claimed, but Mary felt the desertion keenly.

"I must just work harder," she announced, and plunged back into the fray. Yes, there was much to be done!

a taste of power

I think you should come to the Convention in Syracuse with me, Albert," Mary said calmly one evening as they sat down after supper. She as usual was preparing to read the handful of pamphlets and newspaper clippings that had been sent to her, while Albert had at once lost himself in a novel. "Think of visiting the school as a successful alumnus. You used to say you would do that some day."

Albert looked up reluctantly from his book. "That was when I was a lot younger and a great deal more foolish than I am now," he told her coldly. "Undergraduates always dream of such moments of triumph. Graduates know how hollow they are."

"I'd like so much to see Dr. French again," Mary went on. "And I wonder if Mrs. Shaw still has that dreadful place on Bemis Street. It would be a sentimental journey for us, Albert, really. You could see your old friends while I'm busy in the meetings, or of course you could come with me."

"No, thank you," Albert said crisply. "I have more than enough of dress reform at home. I have no desire to see it *en masse*."

Mary laughed. She was disappointed in a way that he wouldn't go to the meeting of the Dress Reform Association with her, but she was glad too. Without him she could devote all of her time and energy to the Convention.

She had been to one of these meetings, and had found the experience exhilarating. For one thing, to her surprise and great pleasure, the people in charge had given her something to do, handing over to her a model dressed in the latest bloomer costume and asking her to talk about it. Later she had reported on the meeting to *Sybil*, the new magazine that concerned itself with the burning questions of the day—burning as far as Mary and the other feminists were concerned—and her statements had appeared in print!

"Albert, look!" she had cried, slapping the magazine down excitedly. He removed it with thumb and forefinger and went back to his novel. "But Albert, they used my report, the whole thing. And Mrs. Hasbrouck wrote that they wanted more from me, anything I cared to write about."

"Fine," said Albert grumpily. "Tell the girls they're all completely crazy. I might even buy a copy and read it, if you'll do that."

Mary paid little attention to his comments. The world, in this year 1857, had suddenly become exciting. She was getting out into it more and more, meeting with intelligent women who had the same ideas and ideals that she did. The busier she became, the better she liked it, and the thought of influencing the course of events in the lives of women everywhere was intoxicating.

Later that year Mary found herself on the speaker's platform for the first time. She was understandably nervous—"But why should you be, my dear Mary? You are living proof of the attractiveness of woman when clad in clothes befitting her life," said the sponsor who met her in Watertown and conducted her to Black River, where she was to lecture. "I hope you forgive my use of your first name, but I feel as though I know you. You and the others who are doing so much for us all are numbered among our

closest friends. And how thrilling it is for us to meet you in person!
I can't believe you could possibly be nervous—not such a strong
and intelligent character as the famous Dr. Mary Walker!"

These kind words gave Mary the courage she needed to go
ahead. She realized, as she stood on the platform, that in spite of
herself she had often been a little self-conscious on the street.
Here she was gaped at not by curious eyes, but by women who
wished they had the courage to do what she had done, longing to
break with the traditions of corsets and long skirts. To be sure,
there were reporters and a few curiosity-seekers, but the general
attitude in the auditorium was friendly and overwhelmingly admiring.

Soon Mary stopped trying to persuade Albert to read her pieces
in *Sybil*, and she no longer asked him to go with her when she
went to one meeting or another. After a while she didn't even tell
him she was going, and when she returned to their home she
picked up her life and her practice as smoothly as possible.

"I know all of this antagonizes Albert," she wrote to Aurora in a
rare burst of candor. "I suppose he's jealous, really, of the success
I have become."

Aurora's policy of leaving her younger sister strictly alone
didn't apply to her marriage.

"Dear, dear Contrary," she wrote back, "is it necessary to make
Albert jealous? I believe you enjoy doing it, and I admonish you to
stop. No man wishes to be inferior to his wife in any way. Albert is
a fine man, and has done much for you. I do think you should be
more considerate."

Mary tried to brush off Aurora's advice, but she acknowledged
to herself that her sister had a point. For a while she tried especially hard to be at home when Albert was there, to consult him
about a patient now and then, and to refrain from mentioning her
successes.

Dress reform, though, was in her blood, and constantly in her
thoughts. Whenever she read a newspaper item that poked fun at
some female who had appeared in public in bloomers, Mary found
herself involuntarily reading the piece out loud. She also used the

slightest excuse to write letters, scattering her shot with abandon.

"Can you imagine spending public funds to fix up an old house, just to make a national monument of it?" she cried, shaking the newspaper angrily. "That's disgraceful! They should take the same sum and build a college for women with it." She glanced at Albert, who gave no sign of having heard her. "I'll write them a letter."

A few days later a front-page story inspired another outcry.

"The latest fashions from Paris, if you please! Why, we have the latest fashions right here in the United States—graceful, healthful fashions. The French had better wake up to what's going on in the world, or they'll find that Paris is no longer, as they claim it is, the fashion capital of the universe. I'll write them a letter." And soon her pen was scribbling furiously.

Another day she cried, "They said that the trio of girls seen strolling in New York in bloomers were hiding their charms. But don't they see the girls were all the more graceful because of their costumes? And what's more, they weren't girls at all, but mature women. They looked like girls, because without all those pounds and pounds of skirts dragging at them they walk better and feel better. I'll write them a letter."

Any accident that could possibly be attributed to the wearing of a conventional costume was grist for her mill. She cut out such stories and pasted the clippings triumphantly in a scrapbook.

"Another woman tripped and fell downstairs—and with a child in her arms. Long skirts, of course. Why can't people see it? And look here," she cried, reaching for the shears and paste pot, "right on the very same page, a woman badly burned and in grave danger of losing her life, because her skirts caught fire when she allowed herself to get too near a fireplace. Probably those despicable hoops that make women look like walking Liberty Bells! I'll write them a letter."

When she wasn't writing letters, she was addressing conventions, or sending articles to *Sybil*. In between these important moments she managed to fit in her practice, such as it was. There wasn't much time left over, and when Albert walked out of the house and didn't come back to it as he had on other occasions, she was forced to admit to herself that she hadn't made many opportunities to be with him. She knew too that her insistence on the importance of that side of her life—the platform and the pen, both dedicated to dress reform—had antagonized him. A pity, too. Albert, she told herself, was not a joiner or a crusader as she was. If only someone could make him see that she was right and he was wrong!

But she wouldn't have changed these last months—she couldn't have. It was all too important to her, and when the Dress-Reform Association made her one of its vice presidents, she knew that it had been well worth what it cost her—even Albert. She moved her office and her home a few doors down the street, and in no time at all felt as though Albert and their four-year alliance had never existed.

"I was never cut out for marriage," she said serenely to Aurora, who had made the trip to Rome just to try to talk her into doing something about Albert. "And I have much too much on my mind to do all the things you say I should do—listen patiently, pretend interest, all of that. Albert has nothing of interest to say, and I do, so it should be the other way around. No, I've made up my mind, Aurora. Not only will I not go after Albert—gracious, as if I would!—but I will make this separation permanent. I shall get a divorce, and nothing you can say will stop me."

"Evvy says to tell you she's sorry this happened to you," Aurora said at last, when she knew her mission had failed.

"Evvy! She's probably delighted! She thinks having a husband is important, so if I'm husbandless, she's glad, not sorry. And for heaven's sake, Aurora, you tell her for me this didn't 'happen to me,' as you put it. I created the situation myself, and it's just what I wanted. You tell her that."

It seemed important to Mary to have Evvy understand that the marriage was ending as she, Mary, wished it. Sometimes Evvy had a way of staring at her with what Mary, thoroughly exasperated, thought could almost be sympathy or, worse, pity. On her rare and brief visits home, she found herself wishing she could avoid Evvy entirely and escape from the look in those brown eyes. Pity from Evvy Barnes Blake, who had never been off the little farm; who had never gone through the first years of school, much less medical college; who was married to an inarticulate farmer whose hands were always dirty and who already, although not yet much over thirty, was bent and gnarled like an old man! While Albert, so straight and distinguished looking——

"Don't you forget!" she cried to Aurora at the railroad station, "to tell Evvy this business about Albert was my idea! And that as soon as I can find the time, I will make it all definite and legal. Don't forget, Aurora!"

Mary chose a little town in Iowa as the place where she would go for her divorce. She had friends there, and because it was near a college town, she thought if she should get tired of merely resting and waiting, she could perhaps take some courses.

"I've always wanted to take up German seriously," she announced, packing the same bags she had arrived with in Syracuse. "There are so many medical and scientific works published in that language, and the little bit I do know fails me when I try to read them. If things get dull, I'll go to the Institute nearby and take some German. It will be good for me to study again."

To no one's surprise, things got dull for her almost immediately, but when Mary enrolled for her German class she hit a snag. The course wasn't to be given, she was told, at least not that term. Mary, now convinced that learning German was the biggest thing in her life, raised a fuss.

"I'll sue the Institute," she said to the woman faculty member to whom she immediately appealed. That there was a woman on the faculty at all had seemed to her to bespeak enlightenment, and she had felt sure that the fortunate female would see things her way. But the woman, Mrs. Oakley, eyed her coldly, frowned at her costume, and told her severely that German was not to be taught, not to Mary or to anyone else, and invited Mary to leave her office.

Mary lifted her chin in a familiar way. "It says right here, in black and white, Course in Elementary German, ten to eleven-

thirty, three days a week. I want to take the course, and you must
offer it."

"We must do no such thing. We have the privilege of withdraw-
ing courses whenever it suits us."

"We'll see about that," Mary snapped. She marched to the door
of the office, then turned back. "I'll take that course in rhetoric
while I'm waiting," she announced.

"The course is not open to women," Mrs. Oakley told her
coldly, and began ostentatiously to write busily in a large ledger.

Mary was furious. Nothing seemed more unjust than having a
member of her own sex make a decision against her that was based
on her sex!

"We'll see about *that* too!" she shouted. As she left the office,
she found several students standing near the door. The undergraduates had laughed at her costume, but she sensed a kind of
grudging admiration all the same, and she decided to take advantage of the moment.

"I suppose you heard all that?" she demanded of the nearest.
He was a tall thin youth who had reminded her, just at first, of
Albert—as Albert had been when she first saw him.

"Most of it, ma'am," he admitted, his eyes shining with amusement.

"Don't worry about it. I'll win. I always win," she told him.

"I expect you do, ma'am," the boy said, nodding. "If you want
to speak, ma'am—I mean if that's why you wanted to get into that
rhetoric class, I have a suggestion."

"Fine. What is it?"

"We've just formed a debating society. We'd be honored to
have you join it."

"Really?" Mary looked up into the young faces around her.
"Would you really?"

"Of course we would. Wouldn't we, men?"

They all nodded and murmured encouragingly. Mary was delighted. "Consider that your club has a new member. Thank you,
gentlemen. I always heard that the men of Iowa have not forgotten chivalry."

She knew they saw her as an amusement, but it didn't worry

her. She had done enough public-speaking so that she was sure
she could hold her own and more with these boys. She realized,
too, that the young men were looking for excitement, and that
they probably suspected she was a firebrand and would provide
some. Just at first, though, she was content to sit back and let them
do the debating. Her time would come.

After their first two meetings, they announced that they were
now ready to hold their first public debate.

"And we want you to be on the team, Miss—er, Dr. Walker."

"No, no, let me take my turn," she protested.

"If you don't speak, maybe no one will come," one of them said
abruptly. The others tried to quiet him, but he insisted on talking.
"We want to charge admission, ma'am. Not much, but enough so
that someday we'll have enough money to challenge other schools
and pay our way to 'em. And if you—if we announce that we have
a lady on the team, and a lady who——"

Mary had a moment of dismay. They wanted her for her freak
value—was that it? Oh, after all, what difference did it make?

"Very well," she told them with her sweetest smile. "I will do
my best, I promise you."

Hand-printed notices appeared around the Institute the next
day, announcing that the new Debating Society would offer a
match on the following Tuesday, and prominent among the names
was that of Dr. Mary E. Walker.

That same afternoon the ringleaders of the Debating Society
were called on the carpet. After quite a session, they found Mary
and told her the news.

"The directress said she was going to suspend you, ma'am,
which doesn't make any sense because you've never been formally
admitted! But you know what we said? We told her we'd walk out
too."

"Oh, no! All of you?"

"All but Eb and Cyril. And they don't matter, anyway. All the
rest of us are standing by you. Come on, ma'am; now we're going
to have some fun."

Before she knew what was happening, Mary found herself the
leading figure in a procession that marched all around the little

town. At first she enjoyed herself, and she was proud of the boys for standing by her, proud of herself for having occasioned this loyalty. But before a sudden rainstorm put an end to the parade, she had second thoughts.

"What am I doing with these boys?" she asked herself. "I'm twenty-eight years old, and these youngsters aren't even twenty yet. I'm too old to be marching about with undergraduates. It proves nothing, does nothing."

Still, it was good sport to stand up to authority—something Mary had always enjoyed doing. After the parade, though, the whole thing fizzled out. The boys, faced with actual suspension from the school, allowed themselves to be talked back to their classes. Two or three of them tried to get the faculty to accept Mary too, but they gave up quickly.

Mary left town—and without her divorce.

"It really was quite an experience," she reported to her sisters back on Bunker Hill Road. "It was fun while it lasted, too. You see, when I was an undergraduate I never had time for such she-nanigans. I was too busy studying medicine, which leaves no room for torchlight parades and student protests. I'm not sorry it happened—it made up, in a way, for what I'd lost. But I own to you, I felt a little ridiculous."

"I should think so," Luna snapped. "One woman and all the rest men."

"No, no, not that," Mary said irritably. "That didn't make any difference. But I was so much older—too old to be acting like an irresponsible student. So I came home."

"And without a divorce," Vesta muttered, after Mary had left the room. "Why do you suppose she didn't wait it out? Did she tell you, Aurora? Contrary usually tells you things."

"No, she didn't. And I for one don't intend to ask her. I don't care to meddle in people's affairs."

Luna and Vesta giggled. "Maybe you don't, Aurora, but you can never say that of our Contrary. Meddling is what she likes to do best. But it is odd about the divorce, isn't it?" said Luna thoughtfully.

"Maybe," Vesta remarked thoughtfully, "she doesn't want the

divorce, really. Perhaps in her heart she's still hoping—she gets a funny little look on her face sometimes. I think maybe it's because she still wishes Albert would come back to her."

"I don't believe that for a minute," Luna said.

"The poor dear, if it is true," murmured Aurora.

Mary made her sisters believe Vesta had been wrong when a little later she again began divorce proceedings, this time in New York State. But again she gave up too soon.

"See?" crowed Vesta. "Just as we thought. She doesn't really want that divorce. Mary never gives up when she's working for something, not if she's truly interested in it."

"Albert was—is—a nice young man," Mrs. Walker remarked sadly. "I think perhaps you're right, Vesta. I wish we could do something about it."

"Poor little Contrary Mary, she must be so alone in the world now." Aurora's good heart was always sympathetic toward her diminutive sister. "Oh, I know she has us. But she'll never settle down here, at least not for a while. And—out there, wherever she is, she's alone. Perhaps she and Albert will make up, Mother. I do hope so."

"They won't," Vesta said sharply. "What man in his right mind would put up with Mary's fancies and her causes? And she'll never change, you know that. But I still wonder why she doesn't go through with the divorce. I suppose we'll never know."

"Not unless she herself decides to tell us," Luna agreed. "Well, at least she always keeps us busy trying to figure her out. What next, I wonder?"

"If those people down South go ahead as they've threatened, Father says there'll be a war," Vesta reminded them. "And in that case, I wouldn't put it past Mary to enlist. Can't you just see her riding a big black horse, shooting from the hip, and telling all the generals how to run their war?"

"Oh, Vesta, stop it!" Luna cried, and they all dissolved in laughter. "What an imagination. Really!"

5

the guns of war

Don't you mind being stared at?"

Mary lifted her pointed chin and unflinchingly met the cold gray eyes that were fastened on hers.

"If I did, I would probably allow myself to ruin my health and wear the foolish dresses you see around you," she retorted. But she wished she could learn—sometimes—to hold her tongue. Her father had warned her often enough that the way to getting what you wanted seldom lay through sharp retorts that could be interpreted, however wrongly, as enmity. "I am accustomed to it," she added calmly.

For once she was vitally interested in something beside the defense of her costume. As soon as the news had spread through the country that Fort Sumter had been fired upon and that there was to be a war between the North and the South, Mary had pointed herself in the direction of just one goal: she intended to be a surgeon in the United States Army, complete with commission, uniform, pay, and prestige.

All applications to Surgeon General Finley had been rejected. Now she was appealing to the Assistant Surgeon. Since her arrival in Washington in October, she had been anything but idle, because wounded and sick men in great need of care and medical aid could be found almost anywhere. Mary had gone first of all to the Patent Office Building.

"They've got it fixed up like a hospital, marble walls and all, and it's got heat and light and lots of space. And they surely need doctors and nurses there, little lady, so if you're what you say you are, you better go over and give them a hand."

That had been the first advice Mary had received in Washington, given her by a Union soldier who had also directed her to a lodging house. At first she thought she had found the key to the success she was seeking.

"I must only call their attention to me, and acquaint them with my knowledge and training, and I'll be on the way to that commission," she had thought, believing that the Surgeon General had refused her because her written application had been signed by someone named Mary and he had, perhaps, thought it a prank.

But it didn't work out that way. Dr. Green, the surgeon in charge at the Patent Office, was in such desperate need of help that he seemed to see neither her bloomers nor her curls. The building, she discovered, contained not only the Patent Office, but a museum and the Department of the Interior, among other things, its several tenants all having been acquired during its twenty years of existence. And the burly soldier who had directed her to it had been right. It was now a sort of hospital, with the wounded men lying in rows on the marble floors, lined up with display cases that were filled with models of the oddities that had been considered worthy of patenting, as well as with curiosities and gifts from foreign countries brought back by explorers. Dr. Green put her to work, watched her quietly for a few minutes, saw that she knew what she was about, and left her. She was sure that he sensed that she was a good worker, that she would labor hard and long, and that she had executive ability which he would at once put to use.

"But I am a doctor," she told him, in one of their rare moments of sitting still. "I should have a commission. I am qualified."

"Probably you are," he said tiredly. "But could you do more than you are doing here?"

Mary stared at his worn face in amazement. She knew well enough that she was saving lives, and making more comfortable hundreds of men who deserved her help, but that was beside the point. She saw herself on the field, performing miracles. She had not forgotten that she had once wanted to emulate Florence Nightingale and go to the Crimea, and that the war there had ended and deprived her of the opportunity. She did not intend to be cheated again, but serving in the city of Washington as an administrative assistant was not what she had come for.

"I gave up my practice in Rome," she said stoutly, "because I expected a commission." She didn't think it worth while telling Dr. Green that her practice had been so small that giving it up wasn't altogether a sacrifice.

"I'll do what I can," he told her wearily. "I'll write a letter for you, if you like. And I advise you to see Wood. He's Assistant Surgeon, and from what I hear he doesn't have as many bees in his bonnet as Finley. Maybe he'll listen to you. I'll see what I can do about getting you in to see him."

Dr. Green had been as good as his word, and he had arranged this interview with Dr. Wood, the man across the desk whose eyes were now fixed on her with such obvious distaste. The session hadn't started favorably, because he took one look at her costume and seemed to withdraw from her, his initial friendly smile dissolving on his craggy face.

"You're accustomed to being stared at. You must be," Dr. Wood said dryly. He gave her one more disdainful look, then glanced at the papers lined up on his desk. "Dr. Green speaks well of you and your work," he admitted grudgingly. "And in your application you state that you have a proper medical degree, and list the subjects that you have studied. I take it that you are truthful in these matters?"

Mary gasped. She wanted to snap an answer, but caught herself in time and said with admirable restraint, "I would be a fool to pretend to know medicine when I did not. It would be easy enough to trap me, wouldn't it? Would you care to test me, sir?"

The cold eyes lifted to her face, and then unexpectedly the smile returned.

"I beg your pardon, ma'am. These days we suspect the worst of everyone, it seems, even of those who are here to help us. And how gravely we need that help. Well, Miss—er, Dr. Walker, if you will return and continue to be useful where Dr. Green says you *are* most helpful, we will see what can be done to improve your status."

Mary returned to the Patent Office triumphant. She felt she had come through the interview with flying colors, and she had confidence in the tired man behind the desk. Her first move was to find another place to live, and then since she was soon to be sent to the battlefront, she decided to make the most of her days in Washington. She wandered about whenever she could, even crossing the river to Virginia where they were building the forts that would defend the city if the Confederates marched toward it as threatened. Everyone in Washington knew that the Confederacy was determined to take Washington, just as the Federal Army intended to take Richmond, and it was universally agreed that if Jefferson Davis sent the Confederate troops against the capital, and if they succeeded in breaking through the defenses, that would be the end of it. So the new fortifications in Alexandria were of great importance.

As she walked about, Mary was stirred by everything she saw. Everyone was busy, working for a common cause. To a woman who had been pitting herself against the world in an effort to build up a practice, it was a thrilling place to be, and a thrilling time to live in.

But she never deserted her duties, and the men in the Patent

Office hospital found her a tower of strength. She even took time out twice to accompany sick soldiers back to their homes, and with Dr. Green's blessing. Although it seemed wrong to devote so much time to an individual, these wounded boys were pathetic, she thought—so young, so homesick.

"Someone had to go," she told an orderly who questioned the usefulness of her trips. "And the men needed a doctor's care on the way, which I was able to give them." She had a way of pulling herself up to her full height when she spoke to her critics, and although her full height was only five feet and sometimes, as in this instance, the critic had an added twelve inches from which to look down on her, it gave her the appearance of authority. On more than one occasion she had asserted herself this way, sometimes saying firmly that she was *Dr.* Walker, and adding that she was a member of the Union Army, and it always seemed to have the desired effect. She didn't stop to think that sheer astonishment had something to do with it—the surprise that came from hearing words spoken with such authority by a tiny woman dressed in an outlandish costume that ended in either bloomers or trousers.

"Father always said if we had confidence in ourselves we would inspire it in others," she murmured, well pleased with herself after such successful encounters.

In addition to her duties at the Patent Office hospital and her long walks around the capital, she discovered there was enough time left over so that she could make other contributions. She was able to round up reading material and games that were welcomed by convalescing soldiers, who found the long hours almost as hard to bear as their wounds and illnesses. And when she had been stopped on the street for the twentieth time or so by a woman who, with fear and despair in her eyes, asked her if she could recommend a place where a room was to be had, she embarked on a new cause.

"These women come here looking for their husbands or their sons," Mary told a new friend, Frances Wright, who had for a time lived in the same rooming house with her. "Some of them can pay, but many can't afford the dreadful prices. Something must be done for them—someone must take care of the poor creatures."

Frances, who had followed her husband to Washington, and Mary had found a small house to rent after a few weeks at the rooming house. Major Wright's duties took him away from the capital much of the time and his wife planned to follow him again, when he was given a permanent duty, but in the meantime the two women lived together, with Mrs. Wright paying the rent while Mary, serving for the time being without pay, hoarded the small sum she had brought with her.

"It's all very well for you to fill up our house with the poor creatures, as you call them," Frances said agreeably, "but this little place can accommodate just so many individuals."

"Then we will find a place where more can be sheltered," Mary said staunchly.

"Easier said than done, my dear."

"Everything can be done, if you put your mind to it," Mary assured her. She marched out into Washington, and before nightfall had found two women, one a widow and both wealthy, with large houses that they were willing to make into temporary hostels. The same women also agreed to round up some of their friends and to form an association that would raise enough money to help out the destitute women and children who roamed the streets in increasing numbers.

"You must of course head up the Association," one of them said.

"I am a doctor," Mary reminded her, "and I have no free time. I must go back to my regular duties."

Before very long Frances Wright began to complain of the cost of feeding the women Mary had sheltered under their roof.

"If they pay a little, I don't mind," she said. "Although the house is terribly full, Mary. If James comes back on leave, we have no bed for him as it is. And the cost of food these days—we can't afford to feed so many."

Mary looked at Frances sharply. Had there been a little added emphasis on the "we"? Mary didn't even carry her own share of the load, much less of the temporary "guests" she had wished on the household.

"I'll see to it," she promised, and using her most authoritative voice and her most confident manner, she succeeded in making sure of a steady supply of food from the Army commissary. "There," she said to Frances, as the first wagon trundled to the door and the load was deposited in the small kitchen. "And there's more where that came from, as much as we need."

That problem solved, Mary turned her attention to herself again.

"My commission," she complained to Dr. Green. "Where is it?"

"This is Washington, my dear," he reminded her. "It takes time."

"Time!" she snapped. "It's been months."

Finally, bored with waiting and annoyed at the lack of recognition, she left the Patent Office hospital to work in a prison on the other side of the city. She tired of that too and went, unexpectedly, to New York where she took some classes in medicine and received another degree. Then, since there had been no change in her standing in Washington and no sign of her commission, she went home to stay with her family.

"Why ever did you go to New York, Mary?" Aurora asked her. "All that studying just now, when you were so badly needed."

"Because—well, I was getting nowhere in Washington," Mary told her. "Day after day they simply put me off. I was working without pay, and working hard."

"But you were doing what you like to do, and you were serving your country."

"They were taking me for granted," Mary said curtly. "Why should they move heaven and earth to get me what I wanted, when I was proving so useful where I was? Besides, I thought a little brush-up in medicine would do me good."

Aurora eyed her small sister thoughtfully. "And beside, you got restless," she said with a smile. "I know you, Contrary. Too long in one place, eh?"

Mary nodded. "In a way, I suppose. But what I say is true. I was just—just stuck there." Also she remembered, although she didn't tell Aurora about it, Frances Wright was beginning to get restive with her full-time job of running a sort of rooming house for nonpaying guests—women who were homesick, or desolate at being separated from their men, or forever asking for help in locating their loved ones. It was Frances Wright's claim that Mary had brought this state of affairs upon them, and she should deal with it, but Mary wanted no part of the day-to-day problems. Escaping to New York had, to put it simply, seemed like a good idea.

Now she took a good look at her surroundings. Here in upper New York State, nothing had changed. Many of the young men from the surrounding farms had gone off to join the Army, but apart from that the war had scarcely touched the area. The summer crops had been a little better than average, so there was a slight sense of prosperity in the farm belt, and Oswego was enjoying an added boom because of its shipping of supplies and food. Mary was indignant.

"Everyone here is stagnating," she said heatedly. "There's a war on."

"It'll be over soon," they told her indulgently. "Don't fret so."

Her father recognized the danger signals. "You want something to do," he told her. "It isn't like you to sit around, and you will get nowhere trying to incite your own family. We know you too well. Why don't you give some lectures in Oswego, while you're here? You've traveled, you have something to offer."

"Wake them up to the war?" she said hopefully. "Yes, why not."

"No, Mary, no one would listen to you. Tell them about Washington, and seeing President Lincoln. And about the President's reception you went to, things like that. Everyone is interested in Washington, and very few people around here have seen it, or ever hope to. You like making speeches, you told me so yourself."

Mary sat down and wrote a lengthy speech that she edited carefully.

As she worked at it, she found that she was directing each sentence to a mental image of Evvy. She weighed each line, conscious of Evvy's brown eyes staring at her, fully aware of the effect every word would have on Evvy's simple mind.

"Because she's the average farm wife," she muttered to herself.

"That's why I think of her now." And knowing that Evvy wouldn't go in to Oswego to hear the talk, Mary went to Evvy's house with the paper in her hand.

"I'm going to give a talk in Oswego, Evvy. I wanted someone to hear it first, to make sure it flows along the way it should. Would you listen?"

"Why not your Ma and Pa?" Evvy demanded. "Or Aurora. Or I suppose you've read it to them a hundred times."

"No, I haven't read it to anyone." Mary was nettled. She read the speech carefully, eying Evvy over the top of the paper. When she had finished, she looked at her friend expectantly.

"You really saw Mr. Lincoln?" Evvy asked. "Is he as tall as they say?"

Mary stared at her speechlessly. "I'll be going back to Washington right after my speech," she said abruptly. "Glad I had a chance to see you, Evvy."

"I heard you were here," Evvy remarked. "I couldn't hardly believe it."

"My family lives here. Why shouldn't I visit them?"

"Too tame for you, I should think." Evvy, who had received Mary grudgingly, now seemed to want to talk. "Wait a minute." She went to the back door and called shrilly, "Come in, all of you. No, Joey, you too." Then she marshaled three pale children into the kitchen, pushing them ahead of her firmly. "Joey, Selma, Louise—this is Miss Dr. Walker. She used to live next door to your mama."

The children stared at the visitor listlessly. Mary knew about Evvy's children, had even seen them at a distance, but she had never before been face to face with them.

"Three?" she murmured. "Is that all, Evvy?"

Evvy pretended to sigh. "It's enough. They're a handful. Run on outside now," she said, and the children all too gladly rushed away.

"They seem nice children," Mary said generously, although she wondered why farm children should be so pale and subdued. "You must bring them to Washington someday, and I'll show them around. Take them to see the White House and the Capitol Building and all. Think how they could brag to their friends!"

Something in Evvy's face changed, as though a door had been slammed behind her eyes. And a moment ago she had seemed so friendly, Mary thought. Why should she glare at me, when I was being so—so good about the children, offering to give up some of my valuable time to show them around Washington?

"Well, I must go," she said briskly. "I have much to do——"

When she gave her speech, it was a moderate success, but she felt that there wasn't much future in this activity, and the old restlessness grew stronger.

"I'm going back to Washington," she announced to her family. "There is much to be done. I can at least look after the boys who are from around here until my commission comes through."

Almost immediately after reaching Washington, she left for Virginia, acting on some halfhearted suggestions that she could make herself useful at General Burnside's headquarters near Warrenton. The General received her as an officer, and she quickly put on the uniform she had had made and had packed just in case; a proper uniform with gold stripes on the blue pants, a gold cord around the felt hat, and—most wonderful touch of all— a green surgeon's sash.

"The wounded and sick should be back in Washington, not here where there aren't enough men to take care of them and hardly any medical supplies," she said to General Burnside who had, somewhat offhandedly, asked her what she thought of the field hospital that had been established at his headquarters.

The General nodded. "No doubt," he said dryly. "How do we get them there?"

"On the cars," she said promptly. "I'll go with them."

General Burnside agreed quickly. He had meant this odd little woman to see the battlefield and to look around, thinking to please her since she had told him she had never seen the Secessionists before, except for Confederates who had been taken prisoner.

"Seceshes don't look much different from the rest of us," he had said. "But go ahead." He knew that the Southerners would look at Mary harder than she looked at them, and he wished he could go along and see their expressions. Now she was repaying his casual kindness by proposing a plan that would take some of the burden of caring for his field hospital off his hands.

"If you think you can do it, go ahead. Send anyone who doesn't cooperate to me."

Mary was just beginning to organize the transfer of the wounded to the railroad train when word came through that the Confederates were going to cut the lines between the camp and Washington. It spread rapidly, as such news always does, and the train was suddenly besieged by all kinds of people determinedly crowding themselves onto the cars, but Mary managed to commandeer a few cars at the end and somehow succeeded in getting her patients on them.

"Why doesn't the train leave?" she asked, after a long wait.

The guard standing below her window shrugged. "Search me," he said. "Ask the engineer."

"All right, I will." Mary, tiny in her blue uniform, marched briskly to the head of the train, ignoring the remarks showered on her from the open windows of the cars. "Why are we standing here?" she demanded of the engineer.

"No authority to move," he told her.

It was the familiar challenge, and rising to it gave her the usual thrill. "You have it now. Start this train at once," she barked.

The engineer gave her a superior grin, the kind of a disrespectful smile that Mary was all too accustomed to.

"Here is my authority, a letter from General Burnside. Now—start the train."

She waited just long enough to see him move his hand toward the throttle, then marched quickly back to her place. Amid cheers and whistles, the train at last moved slowly away.

Back in Washington, she managed to wedge herself into the little house that was filled to overflowing with the women who had found refuge there. She wasn't too pleased to find the guests

spending all of their time sitting about the house discussing the
virtues of their husbands and sons with the others, moaning about
their inability to find them, fussing about the red tape, taking free
food and lodging for granted, and doing nothing whatsoever.

"There is a great deal of work to be done," Mary snapped at
them. They stared at her tiny figure in the resplendent uniform
that she had decided, with some misgivings, to wear in Washington, although she had no paper that said she was entitled to it, and
no bars or buttons to tell her rank. These women were all relative
newcomers, and had never seen little Dr. Walker before, although
word of her had been passed down from the first guests in the
house through each succeeding group.

"Don't gape at me like that," she commanded. "Go out and do
something for other people for a change, instead of sitting here
telling each other your troubles. The city is full of hospitals, and
the hospitals are full of wounded men. Wouldn't you want someone to take care of your man, if he needed it? You, I'm speaking to
you, the one with the red eyes. Since you can't find your husband
for the moment, for goodness' sake go and take care of someone
else's. Maybe God will pay you back. Now, get out of here, all of
you, and go to work—or I'll close the house to you."

She retained one of the most sensible-looking women and gave
her instructions for running the house. Frances Wright who, fortunately, continued to pay the rent, had left Washington three
weeks before Mary's return, and the house was a shambles, untidy
and dirty.

"Get someone to help you dig this place out," Mary commanded. "And you are responsible for seeing that it stays clean
from now on. Make the others follow your orders, and if you have
trouble report to me. While I'm here," she added, for already the
household was getting on her nerves.

She shed her uniform and went to see the Assistant Surgeon
again.

"I'm still waiting for my commission, General Wood," she said.
"You may have forgotten me. I am Dr. Mary E. Walker."

"I haven't forgotten you." His face, she saw, was more deeply lined than ever.

"Someone has, then," she responded tartly. "My commission?"

"I'll have someone run down the application at once," he promised her, and she eyed his face sharply. Did he mean it, or was it lip service he was giving her? she wondered. "In the meantime," he went on, "unofficially—if you want action, and I assume you do—they could use you down in Virginia where General Burnside is——"

"General Burnside!" Mary cried. "But he is—I know him, sir. Thank you, sir."

"Mark the word unofficial," he reminded her sternly. "As for me, I never heard of you."

"Except for pursuing my commission," she said, flashing him a demure smile.

"Except for that," he agreed gravely. "Good day, Dr. Walker."

Mary left Washington as quickly as she could. By the time she reached, on a series of trains and wagons, the banks of the Rappahannock, she found the wounded streaming across the river from the slaughter that was the Battle of Fredericksburg. Now she needed every skill she had as a doctor, and every bit of her determination was required to face up to the horrors that she saw around her. But she was everywhere, doing what she could. At one point she saw injured men being loaded aboard hospital trains to be taken to Washington, and noticed that the stretcher bearers were carrying the wounded down a slope head first. As she hurried to tend to a new load of men being brought in, she ordered the bearers to reverse the litters, to make the wounded more comfortable.

"They take my orders without even blinking," she thought exultantly. "No one sneers or smiles at me now, not here where I am needed."

During the war she was able to forget herself more and more. The bloody battles produced such misery and suffering that they provided her with all the work she could handle. Even Washington, when she returned, was always receiving new waves of men who were not only wounded but ill and usually undernourished. One day, as she hurried along the muddy streets, she happened to witness the arrival of a straggling band of Confederate soldiers taken at the Battle of Chancellorsville. Tired, dressed in rags, obviously starving, these men who had recently been trying to kill their sons and brothers moved even the women of Washington. Lincoln himself was there, and Mary saw that his deep brooding eyes were filled with compassion. She noticed that many of the prisoners had no shoes, some had no coats, all of them looked ready to drop with fatigue.

"Some women standing there took food and water to them," she wrote home afterward. "But the Provost Marshal sent men to stop it. The man is a beast. If I had had anything to offer, I would have gladly given it to the poor lads myself. I believe Father Abraham felt the same way."

Her father wrote back in his square, tidy script that perhaps it was just as well she had been there with empty hands.

"My Contrary Mary might have caused an incident," he wrote, "that would have done nothing whatsoever for the prisoners, and perhaps have gotten her into trouble. I am one of your great admirers, my dear daughter, and have been ever since you announced to me that you would make a lifework out of doctoring the sick in foreign lands. I am still proud of you and the great good you have done for our poor boys after battle. But sometimes I think you forget that hiding under a bushel basket may make a light stronger and more durable. Put that same light out in the wind and—poof—it is gone, and of no use to anyone until it is again lighted."

Mary squirmed a little over that. The one criticism she had ever had from her father had been centered around her willingness to be in the public eye. And yet, she thought, he tells us to be true to ourselves and our beliefs. The two things don't mesh.

She read on: "I have been intensely proud of your stand in the matter of dress, pleased that you took my advice and refused to wear the garments that we feel are so harmful to women. Proud that you can wear your bloomer costume in public with such grace, and pleased with your adoption of men's trousers when you serve on the battlefield, where surely any other garb would be out of place. But never, my dear daughter, give up your femininity. Hide your curls under a hat, when practicality calls for it, but show them, along with your feminine grace, when you can. Never for a moment forget that the more appealing you look, the less queer your dress will appear to the stupid people who refuse to accept change and improvement.

"That was what I meant when I said if you had rushed into the foreground with food for those poor boys, you could have harmed your cause, just as overdoing the masculine attire could harm it. Step along softly, Mary, in spite of what your contrary heart may tell you—and you will win, I am sure of it."

Mary's "contrary heart" was warm as she folded the letter and put it away. She resented interference, even from her father, whom she admired more than anyone else in the world, but Alvah Walker had a way of sugar-coating his suggestions with praise, and she was always susceptible to praise.

"I send you a clipping," she wrote back to him, "from a New York paper. I think you will see that I have not forgotten how to be a feminine person. Indeed, it is quite flattering to your Contrary Mary, is it not? I send it only because I thought it would please you. Myself, I have no time for such bits of journalism!"

6

surgeon walker

Mary looked at the wounded men lying in rows along the side of the road. There was plenty to be done here. It was the third week in September by the time she reached Chattanooga, and the wounded were pouring into the city from Chickamauga, a few miles south.

"They're making one big hospital out of this place," muttered a man in a muddy uniform. He was working over a boy whose wounds shocked even Mary, and she was accustomed by now to the results of close combat. "Can you do anything to help?"

"I'm a doctor," Mary told him calmly. "And I'm here to help."

She took her place among the men who were working feverishly to give at least superficial aid to the wounded and dying. Some of them, she saw, knew little or nothing of medical treatment, but were binding wounds or stanching blood by instinct, or perhaps by watching those who had more skill and knowledge.

"You should see the ones on the other side," one man told her grimly. He had just brought a mule-drawn wagonload of wounded in and, with the help of two soldiers who were themselves wounded but able to walk, was lining them up on the ground. "Those Confeds lying out there on the field. There are thousands of them—a good share already dead, or so close as never mind. General Thomas' men had at them with bayonets, until the reserves came in. I never want to see the like of it again."

Mary worked tirelessly through the day, until the men had been moved from the roadside into the hospitals that had been set up everywhere. It was true enough that Chattanooga was like one big hospital. Every time more wounded were brought in, she heard the same story about the thousands on both sides left by the battle. She wondered if there was anything left of either Army.

As the dusk fell, she retrieved her gear, which she had left on the front porch of a small frame house, and wearily made her way into the city. Eventually she found a group of tents that was pointed out to her as "headquarters," and she was passed from hand to hand until she reached the officer in charge.

"Looks to me like we've already had some of the services you're volunteering," he remarked. "And we need all the help we can get, as you must know by now. If you really are a doctor, so much the better."

Mary was too tired to snap back at him. She stood there silently, her pale face streaked with dirt and her uniform covered with blood and mud until after a compassionate look at her he said, "Jameson, take this—this lady to that house over there. If they haven't got room, tell 'em to make room. Perhaps," he added wryly, "you'd better explain she's a female. One more soldier doesn't mean much to the people here, at this point."

Again Mary was too tired to say anything. The long frustrating trip to Tennessee had seemed endless, filled with unexplained stops, long periods of waiting, cramped quarters, hour after hour spent without food or even water to drink. She had not slept at all the night before, and had plunged immediately into the difficult task of trying to care for badly wounded men under appalling conditions. She followed the orderly numbly, grateful to him

when he took her heavy canvas bag from her and feeling as though
she were walking in her sleep.

A tall angular woman met them at the door.

"This—this lady is to stay here," the orderly said. "Colonel's
orders."

"I got no more room . . . Lady?" The tall woman bent down
and peered nearsightedly at the small figure standing on the
wooden step.

"Of course it's a lady. She can share my room, Mrs. Fallon, if you
have none available. She's so small she can bunk on that sofa by
the window, I am sure."

Mary looked gratefully at the last speaker. She was, in these
surroundings, a creature of elegance, dressed in spotless blue
muslin, her hair carefully arranged. For once Mary paid little attention to the clothes, however, aware only of the warmth of the
voice and the friendly generosity behind it.

"I'm Celia Osborne," the woman said. "Please carry the bag up
to the room at the top of the stairs—there where the door is
open," she added to the orderly. "Wife of Major Osborne. You
look ready to drop. We'll fix you up in my room for the moment,
and then find better quarters for you. Mrs. Fallon, hot water and
clean sheets at once, if you please."

Celia Osborne was just the sort of woman to appeal to Mary.
When she gave orders she expected to have them obeyed, and at
the moment Mary didn't mind obeying herself. After a good
night's sleep she returned to the headquarters nearby and was assigned to her duties. As she suspected, her qualifications weren't
questioned too closely; there was work to be done, and even the
untrained hands that were volunteered were put to use. She
worked quietly and efficiently, and before long had the respect, if
not the admiration, of the men who labored beside her.

"I do admire you," Ceclia Osborne said frequently. "I do indeed. I would be no good at all at that doctoring—the wounds
upset and sicken me. But of course we are all created differently."

Celia, for all she looked as though she would be more at home in
her own parlor back in Connecticut, continued to win Mary's ap-

proval. For one thing, she didn't allow herself to be idle. She orga-
nized all of the women nearby, the Southerners who lived there
and the few Northern wives who had followed their husbands as
she had, and they rolled bandages and picked lint and washed
and mended the soldiers' clothing. Most of them were seldom to
be seen without knitting in their hands. Mary didn't think much of
"camp followers," as she thought of these wives, but since they
were useful here she felt these were different.

Celia, throughout, was her only friend. The men accepted her
help and she knew they acknowledged, most of them, that she had
equal training with them, but they made no effort to know her as a
person, and except for Celia, the women drew away from her.
Mary didn't mind, she was used to it. The only thing that bothered her these days was the same old vexation: she had no commission, no official recognition.

One morning, as she had tended to the last man in the hospital
tent to which she was assigned, an orderly appeared.

"Mrs. Walker, ma'am?" he asked.

"I am Dr. Walker," she said crisply.

"General Thomas wants to see you." Mary's heart beat quickly.
She followed the orderly, knowing that he took long steps and
walked as fast as he could to tease her, and determined not to trot
after him and so appear ridiculous. She walked quickly but with
dignity and forced him finally to slow down.

She was anxious to see this General who had succeeded in turning a certain Union defeat into a victory, although losses on both
sides had been so heavy that the word itself seemed out of place.
To her disappointment, General Thomas himself was not there,
but a man who said he was acting as the General's deputy quizzed
her briefly on her education and experience, and said, "General
Thomas has heard that you have been doing good work here. The
Assistant Surgeon attached to Colonel McCook's Fifty-Second
Ohio Infantry has died, and the post is open. General Thomas
suggests that you fill it."

Mary's eyes sparkled. It was nearly the end of 1863. She had
been trying to get a commission ever since April of 1861, and now,

after two and a half years of hard work, she had achieved her ambition. She was an acknowledged Assistant Surgeon, and from now on she would do what she wanted to do and what life had prepared her for with the full blessing of the authorities.

"This time it will last," she wrote triumphantly to Aurora. "Until now, the generals have availed themselves of my services when they were needed, and have then forgotten me. This time I am attached to a definite unit, with orders and a real standing of my own. At last!"

General Thomas at once became her hero. "They say that at first the Confederates were winning at Chickamauga, but Thomas turned the tide. If they had won here, it could, my friends tell me, have been the end of the war. Imagine! But because of General Thomas the whole Mississippi Valley now belongs to the North. They call Thomas the Rock of Chickamauga, and no wonder."

Only once or twice did the thought cross Mary's mind that her friend Celia Osborne, through her husband, might have persuaded the General to give her the post of which she was so proud, but she always managed to put it out of her head at once. Rewards were for work well done; she deserved the honor and had no need of a friend at camp for string-pulling. And furthermore, she would prove herself worthy of it over and over.

In spite of her elation at the new turn of events, Mary discovered that her life wasn't to be clear sailing after all. Prompted by one of the members of the medical staff attached to the Army of the Cumberland, an investigation was launched against her. She was called names, her schooling and training questioned, and Mary finally was forced to appear before an examining board.

"It was horrible, horrible," Mary moaned to Celia when the hours were behind her. "Every man there condemned me before he so much as saw me. He said to himself, 'Here's a woman who claims to be a doctor, which she can't be because she's a woman.' I saw them there, with their skeptical faces and their ugly closed minds."

"Poor Mary," Celia said sympathetically. "But you must have weathered such storms before."

"Never as—as humiliating as this," she cried out. "They were so many and not one would help or defend me. Before I had a chance to finish answering one of their questions, they had turned the words around so that my answer was meaningless. And they laughed at me. One of them said, 'My wife, who certainly makes no claim to know medicine, could prescribe more ably than that. For that matter, most housewives could do as well.' And they wouldn't listen to me. I've never been so humiliated in my life."

"Why don't you go home?" suggested Celia soothingly. "You've done so much already, you should be satisfied with that and give it up, Mary. If the men, rightly or wrongly, are determined against you, what can you do, one woman, against all of them?"

Those were fighting words to Mary and just what she needed. She blew her nose, scrubbed her handkerchief over her eyes, and lifted her chin.

"Just what I've always done," she retorted. "Keep on the way I am. I'm right, and someday everyone will see it my way. In the meantime, there's much to be done, and I'm going to do it."

And that's what she did. There was no official order for her to leave her post, so she continued to work unceasingly in the hospital and insisted on being Assistant Surgeon in spite of the medical board's finding. The fact that some of her patients seemed to turn away from her determination didn't even bother her.

"Some people will listen to anyone," she maintained. "I notice the ones who really need medical care don't find me so repulsive, or ask to see my doctor's degree before they accept any help from me."

When her work in the hospital was done, she found time to ride away from the city, with its steep streets and the forbidding ridges that frowned down on it, and into the countryside to take care of the families who lived there. Some of them were in hiding, others had for months been eking out an existence without a man to help them, since all able-bodied men of sixteen and over had long since been called up. For a time the Confederates had tried to starve the Union soldiers stationed in Chattanooga, and as a result the nearby farms and homes had been looted of all supplies that could be found, making the lives of these already unhappy people more difficult than ever, and Mary, once she had launched herself on her self-appointed crusade, was determined to do everything she could for them.

She returned from one such ride one day tired and muddy. Her horse had stumbled and Mary, caught off guard, had fallen onto the muddy bank of a creek that had flooded a few days before. Then, trying to avoid another swollen stream, she had been lost for hours. This time she had been away from camp for two days, staying overnight with a widow and her daughter. As usual, the women had been at first distressed by her uniform, not only because it was blue, which meant she was an enemy, but also because there was a woman in those outlandish pants. Finally they had come to accept her and her help, as well as the food in her saddlebags, gratefully.

Mary felt that all of these poor people were pathetic. Soon they became used to having the odd little doctor in the house, their reserves broken down by her soothing touch on feverish foreheads, her salves and unguents on sores and scratches, her pills and powders for stomachs that had rebelled against diets of berries and bark and the tough meat of small wild animals. Once they had accepted her and had ceased to be afraid, they were starved, she found, as much for news of what was going on in the world as they were for proper food.

"We heard the guns," the women would say. "For days and days, the guns. We heard tell a lot of ours were killed. On your side too?"

Mary had heard that each side had suffered as many as fifteen thousand wounded and missing, with close to two thousand killed in each army on the field at Chickamauga alone, and a month later Lookout Mountain and Missionary Ridge had added their toll to the frightening totals. It would do no good to quote such figures to these women, who had so little comprehension of the numbers involved.

"There were many. Too many," she answered them gravely. "But the war is still going on, and the men who escaped being killed or wounded are east of here by now, in Virginia or Pennsylvania. Because your man does not come home doesn't mean that he never will, you know."

She was surprised to find so many of these women sympathizing with the North. "My Joe, he didn't want Secession, not at all, and he was right angered when Tennessee went that way. But when he was called up, he must go, mustn't he? Go to give his life for something as does him no good. My Joe never had no slaves, nor ever wanted none. It's just as he said—this is a rich man's war, but a poor man's fight. When will it end, ma'am, do you think?"

She had to provide sustenance for the spirit as well as for the body, and mend grieving hearts as well as broken bones and the effects of malnutrition, but she felt she would never get accustomed to it.

This last visit had been especially painful to her, because the family that had reluctantly taken her in overnight seemed particularly pathetic. The mother had been widowed in the early part of the war; her husband had been with Beauregard at Bull Run and killed on the first day of the fighting. When the draft had gone through, nearly two years ago, the daughter's sweetheart had hidden himself away, determined not to serve in the Army, but his hiding place had been discovered by a band of Federals. They had marched him away and he had never been heard of again. Since that moment the two women had cut themselves off from their neighbors, and were moving from day to day in a daze of incomprehension and complete hopelessness.

Mary, always impatient with people who couldn't or wouldn't seek to improve their lives, had spent the hours trying to wake them up.

"There are families all over the South that are as badly off as you two," she said again and again. "And in the North too. What good does it do to sit here like this? There are wounded to be cared for; you can do that as well as your neighbors. Supposing that young man of yours comes back and finds you like this, Sue Ellen? Do you think he'd be glad to see you looking like a ghost, with your hair like that? Wash your face and your hair too, for heaven's sake. Curl it. Put on another dress, or if you haven't got one, find some berries you can use to dye this one into something a little more happy than that dirty clay-colored gray. You're still alive, the both of you, whether you want to be or not, and you owe it to yourselves to act as though you knew it."

Whether it was her words, or the food she had for them, or the cleaning she gave their house with their halfhearted help, or whatever it was, she thought they had spruced up while she was there. But it had taken a lot out of Mary. Doctoring people's bodies she didn't mind, and it was never too much work for her. But their broken spirits—it took some of her own spirit away, as though she had given it to them and must somehow manufacture more of her own.

Back at camp, Mary turned her tired and muddy horse over to an orderly and wearily went to her own room, where she found Celia Osborne waiting for her impatiently.

"Mary, wherever have you been? Oh, Mary, what do you suppose they're saying about you now?"

"That I'm really a man and six feet tall," Mary said waspishly. "I thought they'd come to it sooner or later."

"That you're a spy!"

"A spy!" Mary poured water in the washbowl and began to wash the Tennessee mud from her face and hands. "Really, Celia? Who says so?"

"Reverend Stewart." Mrs. Osborne giggled.

"That old gossip!" Mary dried her face carefully. "Now why should he say such a thing?"

"He says you go out through the lines every day. He says you *say* you're tending the sick, but he knows better. I suppose he doubts a Union officer would take care of the Seceshes."

"For a man of the cloth, he has a mighty low opinion of people," Mary said. "It wouldn't hurt him to go out there and give those poor creatures some comfort, if you ask me. Well, let him talk. I guess the men know why I go, and because it's still cold weather there's not so much sickness around here so I can take the time. I wouldn't deprive our boys of any care, and I'm sure they know that. The Reverend Stewart—that old biddy!"

Mary looked in the cracked mirror over her washstand. Her eyes were shining, and her cheeks pink from the cold water and from having been scrubbed dry. She tucked her curls up under her hat when she was outside, but they were tumbled down around her shoulders now. She looked, she thought, more like a spy than a surgeon at the moment!

"There is one thing," she added quietly. "The men here wouldn't dare do what I do. If they were caught by the Confederates they would be taken prisoner."

"Perhaps you will be."

"A woman? Pooh," Mary retorted. "Well, someday they will thank me, you wait and see. One day someone will find out I've done some good here, showing these poor people that Union officers aren't all monsters, but can be kind and helpful to them."

At first Mary wondered somewhat uneasily if there were many who believed the Reverend Stewart's statement about her, but no one looked at her speculatively, to see if she had important documents sewn into her hat or coat, and after a while she forgot it. But the Reverend had also said the men resented her, and Mary resented *that*.

"Some of the men do, of course," she said calmly to Celia. "And the reason is obvious—they don't like to see a woman who knows she's an equal and goes about proving it. Naturally that doesn't go down very well with some of them. Well, it will pass." And she went about her business, both inside and outside of camp, as well as she could.

One day she had a true triumph. There was to be a review of the troops, which Colonel McCook insisted on regularly, and he was suddenly called away. With a twinkle in his eye, but a perfectly straight face, he asked Mary if she would review his regiment for him.

Mary was in heaven. She put on a red sash instead of her customary green one, and, sitting as straight and tall in the saddle as she could, she rode down the lines with an orderly on either side of her, the men standing stiffly at attention, the Stars and Stripes fluttering in the breeze.

For once, she thought triumphantly, I have, although a woman, been given an honor heretofore reserved only for men. And she knew she would never forget the moment.

castle thunder

Celia Osborne had told her often enough that she could at any time be seized as a spy.

"By either side, Mary," she reminded her. "You know full well they've spread the word around here that you're working for the Seceshes. And when the people see you riding on their roads in the Union uniform, they must think you're out to spy on them. Couldn't you at least wear a dress, Mary; not that—that man's uniform?"

"And ride sidesaddle? No thank you! For one thing the guards would never let me out of the gates. Or back in again either, probably, using my dress as an excuse to get rid of me. I'm all right as I am, Celia."

Celia sighed. "You do try me," she murmured. "Really, Mary. I don't wonder your family used to call you Contrary Mary. It is most apt." Then she renewed her attack. "Also, Mary Walker, as you very well know, the people here would do almost anything to get a horse. Commit murder, even. And you carry no arms. One day someone will shoot you just for that old nag the Colonel lets you take."

Mary shrugged it all off. There had been a few incidents during her rides abroad, but she hadn't confided them to Celia. She wouldn't put it past her friend to work on the authorities, through her easygoing major-husband, so that her rides would be stopped. Apart from the good she knew she was doing, she thought she couldn't bear that. Confinement didn't suit her at all, and when she wasn't visiting her patients, or checking up on the convalescents they had moved to Chattanooga, she found time heavy on her hands. The men she worked with never asked her to share their idle hours, and except for Celia, the wives who had followed their husbands to Tennessee gave her a wide berth.

"You would think," Mary remarked coldly to Celia, "that the silly sheep would feel I could not in any way be in competition with them for the affections of their menfolk, since they obviously believe feminine charm is based on the wearing of as many skirts and petticoats as possible, and they would therefore accept me. But I am just as glad. I soon tire of female chatter."

She was grateful to Celia for daring to be friends with her, but her real happiness these days was found outside of camp. The early spring in Tennessee was bountiful, covering the scars of war with tender greens and splashes of pink and white as the dogwood and redbud budded and bloomed, and if she took the time, which she did in spite of herself now and then, she found arbutus and violets, anemone and sweet william, growing sturdily in the silent forest. The countryside around Chattanooga was beautiful, and the hours spent on her horse, riding from one small farm to the next through the spring splendor, pleased her almost as much as did her winning over the people and her ability to help those who needed her.

One day two men rode up to her, demanding food and money. One of them pointed to her saddlebags.

"Have you guns in there?" he asked. "Let me have them."

"I have no arms of any sort," Mary said, and saw the start of surprise the man gave when he heard her high, clear voice. She pulled off her officer's hat in a swift movement that made the man beside her reach for his own gun, and let her curls tumble down over her shoulders.

"A woman! But you still might have guns. Hand over the bags, both of them."

"I am a doctor, a surgeon in the Union Army, and I have only surgical instruments and medicines in here. Let me show you."

The spokesman stared at her hard for a moment. "Never mind," he said, and kicked his thin horse into a gallop, with his companion following suit.

After that, Mary thought sometimes of carrying a gun—she knew how to use one and had done so, on occasion, merely to scare someone who thought to bully her because of her size and sex—but she realized that if she had had a gun it would quickly have been taken from her by these men, and if she had held it ready to use she herself might have been shot on the spot. It was a problem she dared not take to Colonel McCook. He must know of her ramblings around the countryside, because he had allowed her to take the horse, but she was sure if he heard there could be danger in it, he would confine her to the camp.

So she went on, enjoying the spring that came so much earlier to Tennessee than to upstate New York, until one day in April when she took a wrong turn somewhere and found herself confronted by a Confederate sentry. On this occasion she was not wearing her uniform, but her bloomer costume, for which she was glad. She was thankful, too, that she had decided to continue her rides unarmed. She promptly assured the man that she had no gun, and that she was a surgeon tending to the civilian sick.

"Come with me," he said. Mary dismounted, tied her horse to a low branch, and wondered if she would ever see the animal again. It was true enough that the Southerners, long lovers and breeders of horseflesh, were destitute for mounts these days. But there was nothing to be done. She followed the sentry until he handed her over to an officer, who immediately pronounced her a prisoner of war.

At first the experience seemed like a nightmare. She worried about the horse, but was given no reassurance as to its return, or her own, for that matter, but she was elated when the officer commanded a soldier to bring her the surgical instruments and supplies in her saddlebags.

"If you have no competent medical staff, I will be glad to help you," she said with a touch of her old brashness, but the man threw her a disdainful look and she lapsed into silence. She had not believed that Southern officers, whom she had so often heard described as chivalrous, would find it in their hearts to seize and hold a lady, but indications pointed in that direction. For once in her life, Mary wished she had listened to somebody else.

"I didn't believe that foolishness Celia talked, but perhaps I should have paid more attention to her," she murmured to herself, waiting alone and neglected in a small, dingy room. But after the first few hours she began to enjoy the situation. That night she was put under guard into a cabin, where she slept fitfully, getting up now and then to peer out of the single window, hoping some method of escape would present itself to her. The next day they took her to General Hill, and he passed her on to General Johnston. By this time Mary knew that she was indeed a prisoner of war—she could have worn her uniform after all, she thought—and that somewhere ahead lay imprisonment.

At General Johnston's headquarters, Mary repeated her suggestion to help tend the sick, and here her offer was gravely accepted. Under guard, she was allowed to see a few patients. She was also talked to by several officers; although she made herself be friendly and frank with them, she suspected that more than one of them was interested in seeing the diminutive lady doctor who had been captured, rather than in getting answers to their questions about the Union Army, which they didn't succeed in prying out of her anyway. Two or three others told her of their ailments, and she listened solemnly.

"They don't fool me, Simon," she said to her guard, after telling one persistent little man that his symptoms indicated he would be dead within a week. Even though the name she put to the disease was a lengthened version of a word for starvation, and the man was incredibly fat for anyone presumably living on wartime rations, he had turned pale as he left. "That one almost believed me," she said with a chuckle.

"Would he know what it is you said he had?" Simon asked. He was a fresh-faced boy who looked stern but who had, she soon discovered, a twinkle always ready to brighten his eyes. "Simon? Is that your first name or your last?" she had asked, when he presented himself.

"Both, ma'am," he had told her gravely. "I am Simon Simon."

She had liked him at once, and she knew that as soon as he grew accustomed to her bloomers, he had begun to like her, too.

Now she looked at him, pulling a long face, and replied to his question. "He would know what I told him he is suffering from," she said. "At least, I suspect he is a doctor from the way he spoke; so he should, even though I dressed it up for him with some extra syllables that mean nothing. I told him in effect he would presently die of malnutrition."

She went into gales of laughter and Simon joined her.

"That is rich, ma'am," he said when he stopped. "But, ma'am, I tell you over and over, you should not have insisted to him or to anyone that you are an officer in the Army. They will never let you go, but will treat you as they would a man."

"And so they should," snapped Mary. Even to save her own skin she refused to deny her coveted commission. "Don't take on so, Simon. I'm not worried, why should you be?"

The next time she saw Simon, he looked more worried than ever. "We are leaving, ma'am," he said.

"We?"

"You, ma'am. And I am to go, too."

"I'm glad of that," she told him warmly. "Where are we going?"

"I fear to Richmond. Leastwise, that's what I heard tell, although no one said so direct, not to me."

"Richmond! Then I am——"

"A real prisoner. That is what you wanted, isn't it?"

Mary nodded. In a way she longed to be back at her duties, but she knew she'd be ashamed if they just turned her loose. It would mean that they didn't consider her a true officer and that she wasn't worth keeping, was fit only to be tossed back into the sea like a too-small fish. No, she preferred to be a real prisoner, regardless of discomfort or even hardship.

"Yes, Simon," she agreed. "That is what I wanted. Exactly."

"Prison won't be very nice, ma'am."

"I know that. Prisons are never nice. But I was captured and that's where I must go. Besides," she went on, seeing his unhappy face, "they will be a little extra kind to a woman prisoner, I'm sure. When do we leave?"

"Tomorrow. We go over to Georgia, and there we get a train that'll take us to Richmond. That's what I heard."

"I believe you're looking forward to the trip, too," Mary said. "After all, you told me you'd never been away from Tennessee. Now's your chance."

"Yes, ma'am," he said grinning. "It'll take a few days, too, I reckon."

It took a week, and the trip was exciting. At the very first stop the train made, there was a crowd gathered, standing silently and looking up at the windows of the car.

"What are they here for?" she asked Simon. "Oh, go ahead, boy. I won't run away, I promise you. Find out why they're here. Do we have food aboard, or is one of the men important?"

There were other prisoners on the train, but not in the car with Mary. They were up ahead, with the officers and men who were being transferred from Tennessee to Virginia. In Mary's car there were half a dozen military wives who, after an agonized look at Mary's costume and after being told that she was a Northern spy, had drawn quickly away and avoided so much as looking at her. Mary was perfectly happy with Simon and the other guards who came and went, and who all made friends with her almost immediately.

Simon grinned from ear to ear as he hurried back into the car, stumbling over bags and crates.

"It's *you*, ma'am! They heard there was a lady wearing—er—them things——"

"Bloomers, Simon. You must learn to say the word, because soon every woman in the country will wear them. Bloomers."

"Yes, ma'am. And they heard you were a doctor, too, and a spy, maybe, and in the Yankee Army, and they just came down to—well, to see for themselves."

"Then we must give them something to look at!" Mary jumped to her feet. "Come along, Simon. And you too, Carter, and Wilson—and—oh, all of you, my whole color guard!"

She trotted to the rear of the car, went out on the small platform, and smiled and waved at the upturned faces. When she turned around she saw without surprise that the guards behind her looked proud of her importance.

"We must do this whenever the train stops," Mary declared happily. "If these people want to see a Yankee doctor who is also a woman sensibly dressed, we must see to it that they do."

After that, she made a point of chatting with these strangers. "No one laughs at me here, I notice," she murmured to herself. "They are interested as well as curious. I must remember to write Father about it."

At one stop a man jumped aboard the train and appeared at her side in her car, pretending to be ill and asking for help.

"Dizzy," he said. "And in such pain—here. And my breathing——"

"You're a humbug," she told him abruptly, suspecting a ruse immediately. "I seem to be a target for humbugs these days. You should be ashamed of yourself. What's more, I strongly suspect you yourself are a doctor, and you wish to trap me. Isn't that so? Well, if you are testing my knowledge, then I'll tell you what you would be suffering from if those symptoms you described to me were genuine." After her quick recital, the man acknowledged the truth of her suspicions and left, sheepishly.

All of this put Mary in a fine humor, which was quickly dissipated when she reached Richmond. In her mind she had been visualizing a sort of dignified house-arrest for herself, her quarters a charming bedroom in a white-pillared mansion where she would be treated as a favored guest. The ladies of Richmond, she had heard, were unusually gracious. They would cluster around her, and she would explain to them the niceties of dress reform.

"The dusty streets—and so muddy, too, sometimes, I'm sure. And the heat. They do say it becomes very hot in Richmond, and that the hot weeks go on and on. How much more comfortable you good ladies will be once you've discarded those cumbersome, useless petticoats." Oh yes, she would have a wonderful time in Richmond converting the ladies to the cause.

The "white-pillared mansion" proved to be a political prison that had been made out of an old tobacco warehouse, and was named Castle Thunder. "Castle," Mary thought, was a somewhat flattering word for the three-story brick building. Where the "Thunder" came from she didn't know or care, but she soon discovered that a second prison, directly across the street, was called Castle Lightning, and she suspected a misplaced sense of humor. Two blocks farther down Cary Street was the famous Libby Prison, another larger tobacco warehouse filled with Yankee officers. Mary wished desperately to be allowed to go there and tend to the wounded, but she was told curtly that the Confederacy took good care of its prisoners, and her help was neither wanted nor needed.

Mary's roommate, a girl from Mississippi, spent her time dissolved in tears, fussing about the vermin in the mattresses and screaming hysterically at the very sound of the rats and mice that scampered around the bare floors. She was inches taller than Mary and twelve years younger, and Mary hated her for her weaknesses.

"You could at least *try* not to cry like a baby all the time," she said. "Just pretend things aren't so bad, and they'll seem better to you. I just wrote home that I had plenty to eat and a nice clean bed to sleep in."

"I was brought up to tell the truth," Ruth sniffled.

"So was I. But I was also brought up to do what I could to prevent others from being unnecessarily unhappy," Mary snapped. She was disgusted with Ruth. At first she had thought this would be a fine opportunity to recruit a Dress Reform enthusiast who would go back to Mississippi and carry on the Association's work there, but she knew without trying that she couldn't make the girl listen. "Such a dreadful waste of time," she thought crossly.

The food actually was plentiful enough, although monotonous, and she became tired of cornbread and rice, with peas and bacon occasionally. Just for something to do, she called a guard into the room one day and handed him the cornbread she had left untouched on her plate.

"They tell me the misguided people of Richmond are starving to death, and that food is so fantastically expensive many can't afford it. I would be glad to let someone who is worse off than I am have this. I cannot eat another mouthful of this stuff, and in future don't bother to send it to me, but give it to the people who are free to walk around and yet haven't enough to eat."

The guard sneered. "Some of the other prisoners have the same regard for the people of Richmond," he said curtly. "But they don't give 'em what they don't want, they share their food with them regular. Bacon and all," he added.

Mary was only slightly embarrassed. She felt sure that the hated cornbread had been given to someone who needed it, so she had accomplished what she set out to do. She was genuinely astonished when, a few days later, wheat bread appeared on the menu. Encouraged by this, she hammered away at anyone who would listen, saying that the prisoners should have fresh vegetables— even cabbage, she asserted, would be a valuable addition to their diet. And sure enough, soon cabbage was served to them, sometimes as often as three times a week.

"It just happened," she said, for once apparently indifferent to her own power. "Coincidence."

The lack of exercise was one problem that Mary didn't know how to solve. She marched back and forth in their little room all day long, and urged Ruth to do the same, but Ruth spent most of her time sitting miserably on the edge of her verminous bed, occa-

sionally toppling over into a deep sleep of utter weariness. The
air, Mary knew, was bad inside the prison. It was bad enough outside, hot and humid throughout the summer weeks, but still it was
preferable to that in the odorous, stuffy rooms. Sometimes, with
Ruth tossing on her bed, Mary sat or stood in the window or on
the little balcony just outside, trying to get some fresh air into her
lungs. Twice Simon stood below and waved to her, and then was
gone. Gone, she thought, to kill another fresh-faced boy, and to be
himself killed by yet another. Occasionally from the balcony she
saw the Confederates bringing in prisoners of war, and she wondered if they could be friends of hers, boys from Oswego or from
the Ohio 52nd, men who would recognize her, perhaps.

Hoping that sooner or later there would be a familiar face
among them, she always saluted the straggling men below, clutch-
ing in her left hand the American flag Ruth's previous roommate
had left behind and which Mary appropriated for her own.

Her one great purpose through all of these weeks was to get her
own release, and she fired off letter after letter suggesting herself
as a candidate for exchange, reminding everyone she wrote to that
physicians were still sadly needed in this war, and she should be
back treating wounded Union soldiers instead of rotting in a
small, stuffy room in Richmond. She even managed to get herself
an appointment with the Provost Marshal of Richmond, a surly
man who told her brusquely that he might be more inclined to
listen to her if she would dress like a lady and not a freak. As usual,
Mary lost her head and snapped back at him, so further appeal to
Provost Marshal Winder was out of the question.

She thought she had never given up hope, but when the end
finally did come she felt, for the first time in her life, weak with
shock. She had been at Castle Thunder for nearly three months.
In the third week of July her roommate, whose reason for being
there she had never discovered, was taken away amid new floods
of tears and hysterics. With little chance to see or talk to the other
prisoners, Mary never did find out why Ruth had been impris-
oned, what her last name was, where she had been taken and for
what purpose, but she finally reached the reluctant conclusion

that Ruth had been a spy for the North, and if that was true, Mary acknowledged that the girl was a great deal braver than she would have guessed.

"Was it all an act?" Mary asked, staring at the empty bed. "One does not take up espionage unless one expects danger and reprisals and is prepared for them. Could she have been carrying on for my benefit, mine and the guards?"

She was impatient at the thought of having been taken in by someone she had felt to be beneath her notice. Perhaps, after all, there were other ways of being brave. She wondered who would be put into the room with her now, but for weeks she was alone. There was, after all, something of a scarcity of female prisoners; at least one could be thankful for that much.

At last Mary was told that she was to go home, exchanged—to her enormous delight—for a major. When she found out that he was six feet tall, a whole twelve inches higher than herself, she was more pleased than ever.

"Now they are at last admitting my worth," she crowed, writing eagerly to her father of the exchange, knowing it would impress him fully as much as it did herself. And on August 12, she went aboard the *New York*, steaming under a flag of truce down the James to Fortress Monroe at Hampton Roads. With hundreds of other prisoners, she felt as though the old steamer was floating far above the water as they pulled in lungfuls of fresh air, heady after the heavy, foul atmosphere of the prison, and when the ship crossed the invisible line that divided the Confederacy and the Union at Hampton Roads, there wasn't a dry eye aboard the *New York*, including Dr. Mary's. Freedom, fresh air—and the Stars and Stripes floating openly overhead—how long they had waited for this!

8

a medal for mary

Not even the fact that she had been exchanged for a major, which implied both the Confederacy and her own country thought her equal to a man of that rank, could hide from Mary Walker the fact that she had not yet been awarded a surgeon's contract. True, she had served as an assistant surgeon, she had worn the uniform with the green sash, she had worked hard and long doing the work required—but the appointment itself was missing. As soon as she could, Mary renewed her campaign to get what she wanted, but no matter which way she turned, the answer was always the same or, more often, there was no answer at all.

Finally she decided to take her plea to the highest court in the land, to the President himself.

"He can only refuse me," she told her friends. "Everyone else has had a chance, so why shouldn't the President! But Mr. Lincoln is a kind and humanitarian man, and fair in all things. I will point out to him that I have served on the field and in hospitals under battle conditions, and that I have been rejected for a commission simply because I am a woman. He will see it fairly, I feel sure."

She took great pains with her letter. She had seen Abraham Lincoln several times, and had been more impressed with him on each occasion. Now she tried to appeal to the compassionate human being so evident behind the dark, sorrowful face.

In less than a week the letter itself came back. Written at the bottom of it, in the President's own handwriting, was a note that she felt was not worthy of the great man she thought Lincoln to be. After pointing out that the Army's medical department was made up of men who were there because they knew their business, he told her he was reluctant to interfere. But perhaps, he added, sometime she could serve as head of a female ward.

"I shouldn't have put that in about the 'female ward,'" Mary complained bitterly. "I only gave it as an alternative to being commissioned a surgeon with the privilege of serving on the battlefield, as I have been doing, thinking he would see how silly it was that I could perform one service and not the other. And he has turned me down! It isn't fair!"

The President's disappointing letter was dated January 16, 1864, and for nine long months Mary stewed over this final blow to her pride, when suddenly, out of the blue, a bit of paper worth over four hundred dollars came to her. The sum was awarded her for her services from March 11, 1864, to August 23 of the same year.

"For only five months out of all the years I've served," she cried indignantly. "And the ridiculous part of it is, I was in prison for most of that time." She decided she might as well be grateful for small favors, since she apparently couldn't expect big ones, and she suspected that she had Colonel McCook to thank for this money. It came at a good time for her, not that a sum of money wouldn't be gratefully received at almost any time in her life. She had a talent, she recognized, for skating on thin ice financially.

The following month her affairs took an even better turn. She was given that long-awaited contract as Acting Assistant Surgeon in the United States Army, and the commission carried with it a salary of one hundred dollars a month.

"I am now the only female Assistant Surgeon in the Army," she told everyone who would listen to her. She wanted to shout it from the housetops and run the good news on the front page of every newspaper in the country. It was something worth crowing about, and no one knew that better than she.

She packed and waited eagerly for the orders that would send her straight to the middle of the action, most of which seemed to be centered around General Sherman and his march across Georgia. There would be plenty to do in his wake, Mary knew, as stories of the Yankee General's horrible devastation of the state poured in. Instead of being sent to work with the Army under battle conditions, however, Mary found herself assigned to the Women's Prison Hospital in Louisville.

"Your mother," she said to her nephew, Charles Griswold, who was Luna's son, "and your aunts would tell you that I wouldn't be Contrary Mary if I didn't find something to fuss about. I suppose they're right. But surely my talents are wasted here? I'm a good Army surgeon, and yet they dump me in this—this backwater. What are they thinking of?"

"Someone has to be here," Charles said reasonably. He was a tall, thin young man, pale, with light hair and eyelashes and a sprinkling of freckles.

"Charles wasn't meant to be a farmer," Luna had told Mary fondly. "Never in this world. He is like Father—he wants to see the world and find things out for himself. He might even become a doctor, like yourself. Charles's Papa is impatient with him, and I think it wise to separate them, at least for a time. You will take care of him, Mary?"

Mary secretly agreed with Charles's father that Luna babied the boy too much, but she was glad to have her nephew with her in Kentucky. She had no patience with physical weakness, and she was sure that a few months away from an overprotective mother would do Charles all the good in the world. So far he had done nothing but follow his aunt around the prison, shrinking from even the simplest unpleasant tasks that he, as an orderly, was supposed to perform. He did as he was told, but he never acted on his own initiative. Sometimes Mary wondered if Charles was going to prove more of a liability than an asset, but for the moment, at least, she was glad to have someone to talk to.

Mary didn't have enough to do at this post to use up her energy, and she insisted on a brisk walk of an hour or so each day when the weather was fine. One afternoon, as she and Charles were taking their walk outside the prison walls, he began to cough violently. "Dear me, Charles, we really must do something about that cough," Mary said. "It gets worse instead of better."

"It's the climate, I'm afraid," Charles said. Mary looked at him sharply. A cough could be faked, she knew that well enough, and except for it and his pallor he looked healthy enough. Perhaps he didn't like Louisville any better than she did and wanted to be sent home, although, if Luna were telling the truth, Charles and his father didn't get along well, so that seemed unlikely.

Mary forgot Charles and his cough as she turned to the subject of the prison women. "These dreadful women," she said, "get enough to eat, heaven knows, and yet they are forever complaining about the food. Meat every single day, and a turkey dinner with all the trimmings on Thanksgiving. Our soldiers should have this sort of fare, not these women who seem to have no remorse or shame but brag about their misdeeds as though they were competing among themselves for prizes.

"Every single one of them has more to eat at one meal than I did for a week, at Castle Thunder." Mary was off on her favorite theme. Each time she discussed her imprisonment in Richmond, the tale grew longer and much more black. By this time she was down to a handful of peas and a small square of cornbread a day. She didn't notice that Charles's pale face was falling into lines of complete boredom. Mary never tired of telling a tale, and it never occurred to her that her listeners could become weary of it even if she did not.

Again, she spoke of the prisoners. "They're an unruly lot—moody, deceitful, and cruel. Cruel even to each other. Well, one can only hope that a transfer will come through presently. As you said, someone must do the job, but sooner or later somebody will

see the truth of my letters and send a person here who is less
qualified than I am to do a surgeon's work on the battlefield. I
don't suppose," she added, in a burst of candor, "that these
women like me any better than I do them."

"They don't," Charles muttered, and Mary turned to him in
surprise.

"How do you know?" she demanded. "Surely you don't talk
with them, Charles, do you?" Not for the first time she was aware
of the disadvantages of having a sixteen-year-old boy roaming
around among these hard-bitten women, with their coarse
tongues and rough talk. "Do you?"

"No, of course not. They—I see them—well, you know, they
make faces at your back, after you walk by."

"Do they really?"

He looked at his aunt curiously. She sounded almost pleased.

"Yes, I suppose they do. Oh dear, how much time must I waste
on them, I wonder? The war is still going on, and I am needed.
Needed! You know, Charles, I may not have told you this, and
perhaps I shouldn't mention it now, but there are many surgeons
at work in the field today who are using the war as a sort of laboratory. It is true that when hundreds and hundreds of men are
wounded and brought into a field hospital, there isn't time to
stand around and think. Action must be quick, or more lives will
be lost than that of the man lying before you on the table. But
many doctors have one great cure for wounded limbs, and that is
amputation. And that is wrong. Very wrong. If I were there, I
could see to it that as many of our boys as possible were saved
from these butchers."

Poor Charles had heard it all before, many times, but he always
turned even whiter than usual when she discussed a surgeon's
duties with him. Charles would never be a doctor, Mary saw, and
she now thought that except for providing her with companionship, he was doing little or no good here at the prison. A little
later, when he came to her and said that his cough seemed to be
worse, and that his health in general was failing, she could find no
reason to hold him in Louisville. In December she sent him off

under the care of an officer who had been assigned to pick up some men wounded at Nashville, and who was to accompany them North under a flag of truce. Charles could help, a little at least, and in her heart Mary was glad to have him go.

"He wants Luna, to pamper and pet him again," she thought, waving him out of sight. "For his sake, I hope his cough is very much worse, at least temporarily, when he meets up with his father. Poor Charles. Poor Luna, too, I imagine."

She missed Charles more than she had expected to. Except for the times when her tongue ran away with her and she forced him to listen to long monologues he had heard again and again, Charles had been an interesting companion. He had an inquiring mind, and his interest in the countryside and the people around him had been genuine and had often awakened Mary's, breaking through her shell of dislike and indifference.

"He *is* like Father!" she realized in surprise. "I thought Luna invented that idea. Charles looks at everything and absorbs it and, I believe, stores it up in his head. I wonder if he can work with tools and carve and do the things Father always does so well. Perhaps he will be an inventor, too. I wish I had taken more pains with him, when he was here."

With her only companion gone, Mary redoubled her efforts to get out of Louisville and into action, but when at last her transfer came through, after she had spent six long months in Louisville, the new assignment was a disappointment to her, because she found she was next to be put in charge of an orphan asylum in Clarksville, near Nashville. Little though she cared for the post itself, she felt it a step in the right direction, because the war had more than once touched Nashville and undoubtedly would again, and surely she could find someone to appeal to, someone who would get her back on active duty where she belonged.

She had been instructed, in her orders, to take care of families who had settled in or near Nashville for one reason or another. These were strangers to the area and needed the kind of help she could give them, she was told, and Mary plunged at once into her work. It reminded her of the trips into the countryside near

Chattanooga, trips that had led to Richmond and Castle Thunder, and she looked forward to being once again the knight in shining armor riding a white horse.

Being Mary, she worked hard at her duties. But being contrary, she plunged herself into an incident that condemned her in the eyes of the people who lived in Clarksville. News of the surrender of the Confederate Army on April 9 had swept across the country, carrying with it a flood of joyous cries and torrents of tears. In Tennessee there were divided loyalties, and almost everyone seemed to have lost men on one side or the other and frequently both, so that everywhere there were mixed emotions and uncertainty as to whether this was a victory or a defeat. Everyone was, of course, glad that the fighting had stopped, but even that fact would take getting used to, and there were many men to be brought back to their families before it seemed real, and even more who would never come back at all.

Altogether, it was an emotional nation with nerves exposed and tempers taut. When word of Lincoln's assassination reached the far corners of the country, the news was received by some with hysteria, by others with a stolid calm that nothing could pierce. Mary herself, long an admirer of Abraham Lincoln—even though he hadn't given her the commission she had asked him for—felt herself rise to new heights of patriotism. And when on Sunday she went to the Easter service at the Episcopal Church, she saw with distaste that the flowers at the font consisted of a circle of white lilies and one red geranium.

"Those are the Confederate colors, and they want us to realize that the Confederacy may be beaten, but she is still unbowed," she muttered to herself. The people sitting near her were upset by the muttering. They couldn't get the sense of what she said, but they knew somehow that trouble was brewing. She was so odd to look at, to begin with; everyone had seen her striding into the church that morning in her blue uniform, trousers and all, with a tunic that stopped short of her knees and the marks of a major on her shoulders. No one could fail to see her, and would never forget the queer little creature. And now she was sitting there muttering, obviously unhappy about something and apparently going to do more than just mutter about it.

Suddenly in the middle of the service, Mary rose. She marched up the aisle as though bugles were blowing and drums were beating, and with a great flourish placed on the white and red flowers a blue ribbon. Then she strutted back to her place. Those sitting nearest her edged away as far as possible, and the tiny Major sat in apparent isolation, paying no attention to her neighbors but smiling with satisfaction.

The story was all over town, of course. The minister, who had been disturbed by the interruption, had simply removed the ribbon and continued the service. In the evening, he was pleased with the size of his congregation until he realized that it wasn't religious zeal which brought his parishioners to him in such numbers, but a desire to see the odd little woman again.

He earnestly hoped she would not return, but there she was. This time after the service was under way, she walked up the aisle from her seat in the center of the church, placed a bouquet and a small silk American flag at the font, and sat down again. The minister waited his chance and as the choir rose, rustling, to begin a hymn, he scooped up the bouquet and flag and swiftly dropped them behind the rail, out of sight.

The congregation waited in breathless anticipation, but not for long. The little Major marched up the aisle once more, leaned over the rail, picked up the flowers and the flag, replaced them conspicuously, and sat down again in her place, looking around her with the same satisfied smile.

This time the minister decided to let it alone. He had no desire to become one side of an undignified tug of war with the strange little woman, and he was sure that she was more determined than he. All he wanted at the moment was for his service to proceed without additional incident, and for Mary never to return to his church again.

As it turned out, he got both of his wishes, for Mary was soon called back to Washington.

"They like to say I was wearing cavalry boots and that I had pistols in my belt and all that," Mary explained when she gleefully reported on the occasion. "It wasn't true. I thought then and think now they had no right to display the Confederate colors, and there's no need for them to keep on harping on the fact there weren't any blue flowers around, because there were violets everywhere. I picked some to prove it. But what really stirred me up was the lack of feeling only two days after Lincoln's death. If you ask me, the South is getting ready to do everything they can to make life unbearable for us. They forget they've actually been soundly beaten, it seems to me."

In June her war service was officially over, but she wore her uniform with her usual swagger on one more occasion. She decided to go to Richmond for the Fourth of July celebration, and when on the train she overheard a group of men arguing among themselves about who should read the stirring words of the Declaration of Independence as part of the day's ceremonies, she cried in her most ringing voice, "Gentlemen, I—Major Dr. Mary E. Walker— will read it."

They were too astonished to refuse, so surrounded almost entirely by fellow Yankees, she walked up the capitol steps dressed in her surgeon's uniform and read the document in her high, shrill voice.

"Did you go and look at that Castle you were in?" her father asked her. "That prison?"

"I wasn't far from it," Mary told him, "but no, I didn't go to look at it from the outside. I had had enough of it to last me for a lifetime. Beside, it may have been burned. The people set fire to the city themselves, you know, and I heard that the whole of Cary Street between 8th and 18th was burned to the ground. Castle Thunder was so close it may have gone too. Actually, I didn't go to see any of the places I used to think of when I was shut up in that horrid little room. There was a huge hospital there on a hill not far from Castle Thunder, someone told me the biggest in the world, perhaps, with a hundred and fifty or more buildings on acres and acres of land. And a woman named Sally Thompson created a hospital in a private home where they say she performed wonders.

She was the only woman given a Confederate commission, but only a captain's, not a major's. I don't know her background, she may have been just a nurse. But I would have enjoyed talking to her. I didn't go there, though; I'm not quite sure myself why I didn't, now."

After her trip to Richmond, Mary folded away her blue uniform. In a way it stood for all of her contrariness—her obstinacy in the matter of dress as well as her perseverance in the profession she had chosen. Her reluctance in taking it off for good was great.

But the end to this, the best part of her life, was yet to come, and an astonishing finish it proved to be. In January, 1866, she received the Congressional Medal of Honor for Meritorious Service, dated November 11, 1865. From that very moment she wore the bronze medal constantly. It was her greatest treasure, a tangible proof that she and her work had been appreciated.

With the medal was a piece of paper that she treasured as well. It was signed by President Andrew Johnson and Mr. Stanton, the Secretary of War, and it referred to her years of service and even her imprisonment.

"Dear Father," she wrote with a full heart, "My greatest dream has come true. I have been *recognized*—as a person, as a woman, and as a doctor—by my country. What do you think of your Contrary now? To have served one's country well and faithfully, you will tell me, should be enough. But recognition too! Whenever you see me now you will see my precious medal also—I will never again be without it. Be sure and tell Evvy—she is always sure no one appreciates all I do. This should relieve her mind somewhat!"

9

settling down

*E*veryone in the war-weary country had been waiting and praying for the end of the struggle, but when it had come at last, in the spring of 1865, there were many who found it difficult to adjust to peace. Mary was one of those. All around her she saw men going happily back to their farms, to oil the rusty plows and hoes and to start planting the summer's crops, or returning to factories or shops or offices, glad to be free of battle and bloodshed.

But Mary, for all she had spent so much time telling people about her fine medical practice, was at a loss. She knew there was no use in returning to Rome. Her practice there hadn't amounted to much anyway, and the few patients who had stayed with her after her separation from Albert Miller would by now have made other arrangements.

The only thing she could do, she decided, was to set up an office in Washington. The capital city still excited her. It was where things were happening, where important people were.

"You'll never settle down to this," her friend Laura Whiting told her calmly as she looked around the small office Mary had arranged in her new home. "It isn't your style at all, Mary Walker."

"I have been a physician for a great many years," Mary reminded her. "Doctoring is my lifework. You know that very well, Laura."

Laura smoothed her skirts with a self-satisfied air. Mary had decided some time ago that she didn't really like Laura Whiting. For one thing, Laura pretended an interest in dress reform, but she refused to wear bloomers herself.

"Harry will not permit it," she always said primly. Mary snorted. One's husband wasn't supposed to permit or not permit. Wives were, as she tried to point out to Laura, people. They should do as they pleased.

"Yes, I know, I know," Laura retorted. "And that's why you are no longer married yourself. Well, I like being Harry's wife, and if my dressing like other women is going to make my Harry happy, then I will dress that way. I appreciate what you are trying to do, Mary, but I think perhaps you are born ahead of your time. That's all."

That was Harry speaking, Mary thought shrewdly. Most of Laura's comments had first been uttered by Harry Whiting. Although she considered Laura a parrot and a hypocrite, Mary remained friends with her. For one thing, she needed a friend badly in crowded, post-war Washington. The whole country seemed to have flocked there, looking for pensions, back pay, jobs, information on missing or wounded relatives—everyone, in her opinion, had an ax to grind and it must be ground in Washington. Also, Laura's husband owned several small houses, and it was only through Laura's help that Mary had been able to rent one. The city was full to overflowing, rents were exorbitant, and Mary needed a place to live in that she could afford.

So she tolerated Laura Whiting and was even sometimes glad to see her when Laura hurried down the street and called on her, always on her way to a tea or to a meeting in which she would take no part.

"Laura is a taker, not a doer," Mary explained to Laura's friend Margaret Nye. "She seems to enjoy hearing others talk, or watching them accomplish things, but she prefers to sit idly by."

"Unlike you, Mary," Margaret nodded. At the time Mary had taken it as a compliment, but later she wondered if Margaret had meant it to be one. Margaret neither worked on committees nor attended meetings. She was perfectly content to be a social butterfly, in a small way, and let others do her battling for her. Mary also suspected that Margaret Nye paid attention to Mary so that she could say to her friends, "That odd little doctor, you know who I mean? Do you know what she said to me the other day?"

It didn't matter to Mary. Margaret had been useful in finding some furnishings for her office, and if Mary had to repay her by providing conversational material for her dinner parties, that was all right. Soon, she thought, she would have other friends, and better things to do than listen to Margaret and Laura chattering in their empty-headed way.

She looked at Laura narrowly now and said, "What did you mean, I won't 'settle down' to this?" she asked.

"Oh, you can't sit here waiting for patients to come in off the street. I know you better than that, Mary. You must be out and— and doing. Why, only yesterday I heard your name mentioned. It was at that committee meeting about the home for the women who come to the city and have no place to stay. I am not on the committee, of course, but Eudora Withers asked me to go in her stead and to take notes. But I forgot to take paper with me, so she must depend on my memory, which isn't very good, as Harry is forever telling me."

"Who mentioned me?" Mary asked curiously.

"There, you see? You are all at once quite lighted up and interested! Why, it was because of your having established the home in the first place, I believe. I know I said that you were here right now, in Washington, and someone said——" Laura flushed and stopped suddenly.

"Said what? Don't be coy with me, Laura. My feelings are not easily hurt, you know that. Said what?"

"That—that you couldn't be in Washington, because no one had heard you and that you—you usually made quite a lot of noise."

Mary laughed delightedly. "Did they really!" she exclaimed. "Well, of course it's true."

"So I said to the woman next to me—such a love of a hat she had on, I couldn't begin to describe it to you. You would have adored it, Mary, since as you've often agreed your weakness in clothes, if you have one, is hats, although Harry says you have a weakness for clothes as do all women everywhere, but yours takes an—an extreme form."

"A weakness for clothes!" Mary said indignantly. "But I——"

Laura giggled. "Yes, Harry maintains that only a woman intensely interested in clothes could wear the—the things that you do. That if you had had a great deal of money instead of none at all, you would no doubt have been a great leader in the fashion world."

"Well!" exclaimed Mary. Instead of angering her, the idea pleased her. It was true enough that she was very fond of bonnets and spent more money on them than she could really afford. "Well, you tell your precious Harry my interest in clothes is not a weakness, but a desire to see my sex sensibly clothed and——"

"Anyway," Laura interrupted swiftly, "you would have loved that hat. Pretty bonnets are still so hard to come by, although there must be milliners in the city now and soon we will be able to pick and choose. Instead of being worn on the back of her head——"

"Tell me about what the woman next to you said," Mary interrupted, although she was curious about the hat, too.

"I said to *her* that as soon as you had arranged your place you would be out making speeches and all that. And you will. And that's why I told you just now that you wouldn't settle down to a small office and a tiny practice or maybe no practice at all."

"I will have a practice," Mary said crisply. "I am a good doctor and people soon find such things out for themselves. Beside, many women prefer women doctors. You will see."

But Laura had been right, Mary admitted to herself after her friend had left. Life was empty and much too quiet. All at once ideas flooded into Mary's mind. At that very moment her time of being quiet and idle was over—there was much to be done.

The next time Laura dropped in, on this occasion on her way to take tea with Senator Amos' wife—"I am simply perishing to see her house," she said, in a flutter of feathers and silks. "I am told she has the finest drawing room in all Washington, filled with French furniture and exquisite bits of French porcelain. Harry has done the Senator a few favors, you see," she added, stroking her tight kid gloves happily, "and now he wants something in return. I am to be very nice to the Senator's wife, he told me. You see, a devoted wife can be very useful to a man in Harry's position."

"Laura," Mary said when her caller stopped for breath, "when will you go to a meeting of the committee again, the one you spoke of Monday?"

"Perhaps never. I don't care too much for those women. They are so—so stodgy."

Mary nodded with understanding. Laura had other fish to fry now; she planned to move in senatorial circles, and she obviously found this much more pleasant than sitting on the sidelines as good women did their best to help the unfortunate. Still, senators and their wives were very often helpful to all sorts of causes, as Mary very well knew.

"Senator Amos, he's on that pension committee, isn't he?"

"I suppose so," Laura answered indifferently. "He's a very busy man, Harry says. And important, too."

"I must meet his wife," Mary murmured, more to herself than to Laura, but her visitor heard her and immediately cried in alarm, "Oh Mary, you see I—well, it happens I was invited especially, I could not take you because——"

"Don't get so upset," Mary said soothingly. "I didn't mean for you to take me with you this afternoon. Or ever, for that matter. Now that I think about it, I will do better to go direct to the Senator, instead of trying to reach him through his wife. I know all about approaching senators," she added proudly. "Anyone could tell you that."

It was true. She was a well-known figure around Washington, and had been almost from the start. The only strange thing about her situation now was that she had been in the city so long and had not again begun her assault on Congress.

She was ready. Forgetting the small office she had found and equipped with such difficulty, Mary sailed out into Washington's mainstream. She was fighting not only for herself, but for women everywhere. First of all she tackled the men who were influential where taxes were concerned.

"No woman earning less than five hundred dollars a year should be taxed in any way," was her cry. "A woman is underpaid to begin with. If she is trying to support herself on such a paltry sum, she should not have any part of it taken from her. A woman who is earning her own livelihood is or should be the head of a household, and treated as such."

They became sick to death of her, and she knew it, but she never let up, and finally she had the satisfaction of success. At the same time she waged a war in behalf of the nurses who had served their country through the war. These women were doing what they could to get pensions for themselves.

"Twenty dollars a month!" cried Mary. "Is that all you're asking for? You should be insulted, really. You've given months or even years of your lives working under appalling conditions. I know, because I was there too. I was an officer of the United States Army, to be sure, so my situation is a little different, but I worked side by side with many of you and I know what you accomplished. Don't be satisfied with the paltry sum of twenty dollars—you price yourselves and your services much too low. I will make it my business to see that you get what you deserve."

She quickly rounded up a group of women who would help her put through a petition. Some of them were nurses, but many were not. Armed with names, case histories, letters, all the ammunition she could get, Mary was caught up once again in the excitement of calling on senators, representatives, committees, even the White

House, begging, pleading, storming, shouting. The acquisition of
patients was all but forgotten.

This time she didn't get what she wanted. The bill was intro-
duced into Congress, and although they were hopeful, not even
the women who had worked on it so hard were entirely surprised
to find it tabled.

"At least," Mary said, "we tried. We didn't sit back. We tried."

While she was flying around attempting to ram through her
pension plan, Mary heard from an old friend, Lydia Hasbrouck,
who had once bought so many articles from Mary for her *Sybil*,
and who urged her now to plunge herself back into the dress reform question, as well as the new cause that was becoming so
prominent, the right of women to vote.

"Why don't you go back on the lecture platform, my dear
Mary," she suggested. "You can do so much good for all of us if
you do."

Mary needed little urging. After she had discarded her uniform
with such reluctance, she had not gone back into her bloomer costume but now dressed in a frock coat and striped trousers. In the
evening, she wore a dress suit. And day and night she still wore
her hair in curls.

She was by this time so accustomed to walking around the
streets of Washington that she had succeeded in persuading herself that people didn't notice her any more. When men made comments she pretended not to hear them—and often she didn't, so
engrossed was she in whatever project occupied her mind at the
moment. When little boys followed her, jeering and chanting, she
hardly noticed. The only times she bothered to make an issue out
of someone else's bad behavior were when she was sure it would
do the cause of Women's Dress Reform some good. Then, when an
occasion presented itself, she always took advantage of it.

Such an opportunity popped up one day when she was in New
York, where she had gone to talk to some new recruits who were
looking for advice and direction. She had returned to her bloomer
costume for the trip, knowing that the new members of the Association would get needed courage from seeing her dressed as they

were, or hoped to be soon. She was shopping near Broadway, fully preoccupied with looking at hats. The owner of the millinery shop had not been too happy when the diminutive figure, dressed so oddly, had appeared at his door, and he was only too anxious to have her leave.

"Madam," he said nervously, as she calmly tried on a pert straw hat with cherry-colored ribbons, turning her head this way and that to see the effect in the mirror. "Madam, you are drawing quite a crowd. They could become unruly, you know. I beg of you to go your way as quickly as possible, before something happens to you."

"Happens to your shop, I suppose you mean," Mary said coldly. She removed the hat, looked at it carefully, and put it down. "The brim is too wide for me, I fear. Kindly hand me that green one, with the curled feather. Yes, this will be better."

He gave her the hat, but he glanced nervously over his shoulder. "Madam, they are still there, looking at you. And more coming. I ask you please to leave."

"I am a citizen, I have as much right on these sidewalks and in these shops as those stupid gaping people out there. Don't look at them, they will get tired of it and go away."

With a gasp of impatience the man turned from her, and Mary thought she had satisfied him, but he pushed his way out through the people who had collected outside and returned almost immediately with a policeman.

"What's this? What's this? You must come with me, ma'am," said the policeman, after verifying with his own eyes the incredible statement made by the shop owner that there was a woman in his place trying on hats calmly who was wearing Turkish trousers and causing a crowd to collect. "You are disturbing the peace, ma'am, and this gentleman has warned you. You must come with me."

"Where to?" Mary demanded belligerently.

"To the station."

She jumped to her feet, smiling. "Good," she said. "I would like nothing better. As for you, I don't like your hats anyway," she said

to the shopkeeper, and walked away with dignity. The crowd
parted silently to let her through, followed by the red-faced policeman who quite obviously wished he had been given duty elsewhere that day. The little lady looked a handful and no mistake,
and he was glad to hand her over to the sergeant on the desk.

"And what brought you here?" the sergeant asked sternly.

"He did, that—that creature!" Mary said, pointing to the policeman whose face grew even redder.

"Why?"

"Ask him. It wasn't my idea."

"Disturbing the peace," the policeman said quickly.

"Disturbing the peace! I like that. Did I make a noise, or create
any disturbance whatsoever? No, indeed, I did not. I was in a
shop, trying on bonnets. And they weren't really very good ones,
either."

"She collected a crowd," the policeman said to the sergeant.

"Then arrest them for disturbing the peace!" Mary snapped. "If
you must get your hands on someone."

"Why are you dressed like that?" The sergeant saw his mistake
almost immediately, because he was treated to a twenty-minute
lecture on dress reform that he was unable to turn off. "And I'm
only sorry that I haven't on my striped trousers and frock coat,"
Mary added, "because then you could say I was masquerading as
a man, and I could prove to you that I was not, showing you the
license to wear trousers which was given me by Congress. I have
been in the White House many times, I will have you know,
dressed as I am now or in trousers, and the President and his
guests are always most happy to see me, nor do they say I am disturbing anybody's peace." It was true enough, as far as it went,
but she didn't say that although many stared at her, few spoke to
little Dr. Walker. Perhaps she hadn't noticed.

The sergeant managed to get a word in. "A license—" he asked
faintly.

"Yes, a license." It wasn't true at all that she had such a license.
Several of the senators with whom she had done business had jok-
ingly told her that Congress should issue her such a document,
and she had spoken of it so often that by now she almost believed

it to be true. "And you would be more embarrassed than you are now," she finished triumphantly.

The sergeant was indeed embarrassed. He threw a black look at the policeman who had caused the trouble and said, "You are free to go," stiffly to Mary.

"Thank you. And what is your name, my good man?" she asked the policeman briskly. "I will have you in court for this. Improper conduct. Very improper, indeed."

She marched out and found a lawyer, who filed the charges. He was the brother of one of her dress reform associates and presumably accustomed to ladies with bees in their bonnets, but Mary could see that he acted with great reluctance. He found out soon enough that he didn't have to worry; Mary was perfectly capable of conducting her own case.

The newspapers loved it. Mary showed up in court dressed in black broadcloth, her skirt above her knees, her trousers loosely fitting, her curls in place. Although she was in court to discuss the conduct of the unhappy policeman, she used the opportunity, as she always did whenever she had an audience, to make a speech on dress reform.

Finally the policeman's counsel, who had trouble concealing the fact that he was enjoying the matter as much as everyone else, got her back on the track, but the whole hearing was a farce that ended in laughter all around when the commissioner who was hearing the case told the policeman not to arrest her again.

The incident improved Mary's position at once, because now she was back in the limelight. A couple of weeks later she went to a convention of the National Dress Reform Association where her recent escapade was on everyone's lips, and where she was elected president for the coming year. She made two speeches and illustrated the one on dress reform by showing live models wearing the favored costume—and she appointed herself as one of her own models.

Mary returned to Washington well pleased. She was a national celebrity, which in itself was gratifying. But—more important—there was work to be done.

10

to see and be seen

Mary eyed Laura's new silk frock coldly.

"Whatever you paid for that foolish dress would feed a family for weeks," Mary remarked. "Or help a widow and her children get on their feet and ready to face life again."

"Or pay your rent, I suppose." Sometimes Laura seemed to forget that she was a friend, and those occasions, Mary was just beginning to realize, were usually related to money. She was indeed behind in her rent, owing Laura's husband three months' now, and twice she had borrowed small sums from Laura herself, but the last time she tried, she had been refused.

Harry Whiting was one of those people who seemed to make money at every turn. He owned real estate in Washington, admitted to an interest in two or three New England textile mills, and seemed always to have so much time for politics that Mary wondered if he wasn't somehow earning still more money by doing favors for politicians. He might even, she thought scornfully, be mixed up in the disgraceful business of the Reconstruction down south. Congress had reversed the original generous terms and had begun to treat the South as a conquered country, sucking from the nearly bloodless body of the Confederacy every bit of life it could, and individual Northerners were growing suddenly very prosperous. It was one of the many injustices on Mary's list now.

Her personal situation wasn't much better than that of the South, she reflected grimly. When she took time out from whatever interested her at the moment and ferreted out a new patient, usually someone who was working on one of her numerous committees, the patient appeared to think treatment and medical advice came free these days. Mary seldom worried about her day-to-day finances—something always came along to save her—but on occasion, and this was one of them, she was frightened by what she saw. The four hundred dollars given her by the government two years before, in September of 1864, had vanished in the first few months, for she had an unfortunate habit of spending money when she had it, on others as well as on herself, and she had found many destitute women in Washington after the war. The last time she had borrowed from Laura, she had persuaded her friend that if she believed in dress reform, as she said, but was unwilling to suit her actions to her words, the very least she could do was send to the Dress Reform Convention a delegate who was actively carrying on the great work. Laura had given her the money, but had made it clear that this would be the last "loan" she would make.

It was September again, and the hot, sultry Washington summer had been hard on Mary. Many of her friends and acquaintances had gone north, or to the hills or the shore to escape the heat, but Mary had stayed in the city, working hard at her innumerable causes even though Congress was adjourned. There was always plenty to do, although little enough in her own office. She was tired, she had lost weight, there were new lines in her face that made her realize that she was, after all, thirty-four years old, and she wanted a rest. Sometimes the thought of the farm on Bunker Hill Road seemed like heaven to her, and she could imagine the cool green shadows under the trees, and the breezes blowing from the lake. It was frightening to think she didn't have even enough money to get there. She looked at Laura's pretty rustling dress enviously. For a fleeting moment she thought of Albert. Was he prosperous too? She was still only separated, not divorced, from Albert, and she knew he had written to Lyman Coats, Aurora's husband, and had asked about her well-being. Aurora had written her that.

Lyman, by marrying Aurora, had become the head of the family in a way, even though Alvah Walker was still alive. Lyman was a businessman, for one thing, which Mary's father had never been. And no one considered it strange that Albert addressed himself to Aurora's husband rather than his father-in-law when legal matters relevant to his separation from Mary came up.

When Aurora wrote Mary that Albert had inquired about her, Mary became angry.

"Don't mention him again," she wrote back to her sister. "Not ever."

By this time she had almost forgotten why she and Albert had parted. Was it because she herself had failed in some way? But of course not—Albert had failed her—had not measured up as a husband.

Evvy Blake, who had run over to visit for an hour or so the last time Mary was at the farm, obviously still thought it was Mary's fault.

"Mary, every one of your sisters is married, and happily," she had pointed out. "They must have told you that you have to work at a marriage, to make it last. Everyone does. But you—well, knowing you, I suppose you figured your Albert was the one who must do all the work."

"Nonsense," Mary had snapped. "I worked much harder. I ran the house, I had a doctor's practice, and patients to call upon in their homes whenever they needed me. I worked even harder than Albert."

Evvy pushed back her graying hair. "I didn't mean that, Mary

Walker, and you very well know it. I meant work at the *marriage.*
You expect everyone to see things your way, and you get impatient if they don't. Oh, I've seen you glare at me when we disagreed about things. I suppose if Albert told you how to doctor a patient, you flew at him."

"Albert wouldn't dream of telling me how to treat a patient,"
Mary, outraged, protested. "He didn't interfere with my patients, and I didn't interfere with his."

"And if Albert didn't like you wearing those pants and said so, I suppose you——"

"Albert was a great disappointment to me!" Mary cried angrily.
"I thought, with his intelligence and his education, he would be an understanding person. Instead he was as narrow-minded and prejudiced as—as a farmer!"

"So it was about the pants." Evvy nodded. "I'm not surprised,
Mary. You could have tried to please him. You could have dressed the way normal women do."

"Never!"

Evvy gazed thoughtfully at Mary's angry face. "Poor Albert,"
she said at last. "And poor you, Mary. It must be—well, very sad to be so stubborn. You pay a big price for it, don't you? I'm sorry,
Mary, truly I am."

"Don't feel sorry for me," Mary told her flatly. "Evvy has never understood me one bit," she thought with anger. "And I've told her and told her, but she won't listen. Imagine being sorry for *me*
—but then, Evvy always was a fool."

Except for moments like this one, Mary managed to forget Albert. And moments like this, the rare ones when she almost acknowledged to herself that she would like someone to lean on a little, were rare and fortunately the weakness soon passed.

"Well," said Laura, rising with a rustle, "I have an errand to do,
and then a call to make. One is so busy these days. It is wonderful to have things settle down into a peacetime pattern again." She swished out of Mary's room with a condescending smile. Peacetime! How Mary longed for the years just past, the busy, important days of nursing wounded men, of riding around the Ten-

nessee countryside helping the sick. She would even, she thought with a smile at herself, like to see Castle Thunder again!

A few days later a letter came that changed everything. At first Mary couldn't believe her good fortune. She was invited to go to England to be a delegate there at a social science congress in Manchester. Mary was ecstatic. Not only was this supreme recognition of her activities and talents, it would give her a chance to mingle with the women of England who were as interested as she was in seeing women's civil rights furthered. She could even, she thought, see something of the big English hospitals, where she was sure techniques were superior to those in this country. Then when she came back, she would have an added inducement to encourage patients to seek her out. "Dr. Mary E. Walker returns from a tour of English hospitals and a profound study of the modern treatments and advanced techniques now practiced abroad. . . ." She would take an advertisement in the paper, to tell all of Washington about her increased knowledge.

On top of all of this, she was thrilled at the prospect of going to Europe. Her father, who considered himself widely traveled in his own country, although he had gone no farther west than New Orleans, had always told her that travel was an education in itself.

"People live differently in other parts of the world. They think differently. You listen to them and observe them and you have added something to yourself."

Up until this morning, Mary had considered that she herself had traveled. Hadn't she gone by train and coach and boat around the South, nursing and working with men from just about every state in the Union? And living in Washington, rubbing elbows with the great and near-great of the nation, was a form of travel, too. But now she saw this wasn't enough. America was a huge country, with handfuls of people scattered along its coasts, rivers, and lakes, and great spaces in between. This, she thought, makes Americans small and provincial. Besides, Americans right now were too busy picking up the pieces after a disastrous war to develop culturally or spiritually. In England she would meet people who were building on firm old foundations, looking forward to the future with knowledgeable, intelligent eyes. She might even, she thought happily, go to the Continent and see something of it, while she was so close!

She wasted no time at all in closing her office and selling everything she could to provide herself with passage and a little pin money. Then she packed up her things and left on the first boat for England. The Convention wasn't to be held for several weeks, so she would do some sightseeing first. She hadn't been over there a week before she realized that while she was seeing the sights, the people of Scotland and England were looking hard at her in her unusual costume. She loved every minute of it.

In October she went to the Congress in Manchester, and on the very first day was called upon to speak. The newspapers discussed her at length, describing her dress in detail and in general were complimentary. Mary clipped one piece and sent it home. She had discovered just recently that whenever anything happened to her that made her glow with pride, she sent the news to her father immediately.

"It pleases him so," she explained to herself, "to find his teachings have borne fruit." But in a more honest moment she admitted reluctantly that she had more selfish reasons than that. Used as she was to ridicule, it still smarted a little sometimes, and furthermore, her greatest triumphs often were moments that did not impress the Laura Whitings of the world, yet it was with such women she was often thrown. As for her own kind, the dress reform and women's suffrage enthusiasts, they viewed her honors with approval and even a little jealousy sometimes, but after all, they expected them of her. In her father she had, she knew, a truly appreciative individual, someone who admired and respected what she had done, and was always ready to praise her.

It was the praise she was after, to counteract the sharp criticisms and the ridicule. When she realized that about herself, Mary was shocked, and she determined not to seek praise hereafter. But now, in England, she felt she must let her family know how successful she was in her great undertaking, and as each newspaper story appeared, describing in glowing terms her trousers, her curls, her modish little hats, she mailed it home, calming her conscience by sending the most recent stories to Aurora rather than to her father.

She could imagine Aurora sitting at the scrubbed table in her sunny kitchen, everything so neat and shining, reading Mary's latest clipping with a smile on her lips, then hitching up her big black horse and clattering over the quiet, dusty roads to her father's farm on Bunker Hill Road. Her parents would pore over the bit of paper and exclaim over their Contrary's success, and then Luna and Vesta would drop by and read it, too. Mary seldom thought about Cynthia, although she was nearest her own age. Of them all, Cynthia was the least adventuresome, the most "normal." She had married an Oswego boy and she lived not far from the others, but she seldom visited them, and she openly criticized Mary's notoriety.

"She is a foundling," Cynthia had remarked once when Mary had written home of being arrested in Washington years before for "impersonating a male," "She should be stopped, she will disgrace us all. Father, *do* something. She *must* be a foundling."

It was Cynthia, Mary thought when the statement was reported to her later, who was the foundling, having no place in an intellectual and forward-thinking family. So Mary put Cynthia out of the family in her own mind, and when she pictured them all together, there was only a shadow in one of the chairs and sometimes not even that.

So she gaily sent home clippings about Dr. Walker and her clothes as they appeared in the English papers. "Be sure to tell Evvy," she wrote in every letter. It always seemed essential for Evvy to know of each fresh triumph. Twice she sat down and wrote long letters to Evvy, describing the sights she had seen, adding, "Tell your children, Evvy. It will give them a glimpse of the world and will do them much good."

She couldn't resist throwing in little comments about her own successes. "After all," she excused herself, "I wouldn't be here at all, seeing the British Isles and everything, if it weren't for my lectures and the Convention. It will give poor Evvy a little vicarious pleasure, just reading about my exciting days here."

Occasionally when she wrote to Aurora, she enclosed clippings on the speeches that she gave, but only occasionally. The press seemed to be much more interested in her trousers than in what she had to say. But the audiences liked her speeches, and showered her with questions. Mary especially enjoyed the question period at the end of her talks. She had a talent for caustic replies, and her quick mind and sharp sense of humor pleased her audiences enormously.

"She is," one paper stated, "the mistress of the perfect retort, and has flattened her critics neatly with a few well-chosen words on many an occasion." Mary put that bit into one of her letters, but she neglected to include the second half of the reporter's reaction to her speech, because he said, "For all the little lady presents an unusual picture on the stage, it is unfortunate that when she opens her mouth the same old trite and tired comments on petticoats seem to issue forth."

But she was able to say truthfully in her letters, "The people love me, and heap flattery upon me. And they are being so kind to me, you couldn't imagine how kind. I am invited everywhere, to speak at the other big cities here on the British Isles, not just in England. To stay with them in their homes. And—what is most important to me, of course—to visit many of their big hospitals."

At each of the major hospitals that she visited, she was usually conducted about the wards and operating rooms by the chiefs of staff themselves, and as she saw with her own eyes the new techniques and the modern methods of surgery, she was amazed at the differences in these operations and those she had witnessed in tents and makeshift quarters in the field of battle. And of course she willingly volunteered information on what she had learned in her own country.

"The speed with which we were forced to work made it imperative for us to find new ways of dealing with old problems," she said frequently, always the center of curious and usually admiring male eyes. These doctors, she thought proudly, accepted her at face value, and were not trying to test or discredit her. "And of course we had many new and unusual problems to solve. As you gentlemen very well know, wars and wounded men tend to increase knowledge. We learned much. But I can't tell you how impressed I have been with the tremendous strides you have made here, greater than those taken by our own big institutions." She didn't think to tell them that she had not taken the opportunity to visit the institutions she thus tossed aside so casually. That didn't seem to matter anyway.

The hospitality of the English went beyond Mary's fondest hopes. She made immediate friends with a couple who were American, but who made their home in England where the Reverend Denison had a church. She used the Denison home as a stopping-off place between trips to Bristol and Edinburgh and the other sites of her speaking engagements, and later they not only planned her trip to Paris but went along with her.

For a while she worked in as much sightseeing as she could, but in November she took up lecturing in earnest, leading off with one given in St. James's Hall.

"Are you sure, my dear Mary," asked the Reverend Denison anxiously, "that this is wise? I know how successful you have been in the past, but don't forget you were talking to women who were already interested in your subject. They were prepared to agree enthusiastically with anything you said before you so much as opened your mouth. But if you speak at St. James's, you will have a motley crowd to sway. Some will be there out of curiosity only, and many will be on hand, I am afraid, merely for the purpose of making remarks that will not be pleasant. And what is more, they will have paid out their hard-earned shillings to get in to hear and see you, and that will make them especially critical. Don't you think it would be wise to content yourself with the field in which you are already a shining light?"

"I appreciate what you are trying to tell me," Mary told him good-naturedly. "And I am well aware of the risks involved. But I will never know until I try, will I? And furthermore, I am committed."

In St. James's Hall she told her story simply. It was a large audience, and a noisy one that frequently interrupted her, but in general they received her well. When she launched into a heated discussion of the rights and wrongs of the Civil War, she found them singularly uninterested, although she held their attention as she told of her own experiences.

"You were right and I was wrong, my dear Mary," the Reverend Denison said to her later. "You held them throughout."

"Throughout an hour and a half!" his wife chirped. "You were splendid, Mary, just splendid."

Mary was tired but exhilarated, and she immediately signed up for more lectures. However, the papers, as well as her friends, occasionally suggested that she spend less time on her pet theme, women's dress. Mary was at first indignant, but it was pointed out to her that she had material enough for several lectures, and that it should be cut apart and used, in sections, in addressing special audiences.

"But you must listen to me, Dr. Mary," said Millicent Jeffers, a friend of the Denisons and a great admirer of Mary's. Mrs. Jeffers had crusaded so long and arduously for women's suffrage that she was known to the press as Militant Millicent, and she reveled in her title. She was a large woman, very tall, and Mary found herself more than once wishing that her new friend would remain seated at all times so that Mary wouldn't get a crick in her neck looking up at her.

"There is absolutely no point," Millicent went on, "in trying to sell these people on dress reform. Oh yes, I know that you've made a conquest of me. And of many other women, too, since you've been here. I own I never thought much about the way we dress, until you pointed out the evils to me, but then I have been so busy trying to explain our rights to the stupid men who won't listen. If they only knew——"

Mary held up her hand. "Don't make your speech to me, Millicent, I know all about it, remember? I already agree with you. And I'm glad that I have made you see the light on dress reform. The two go hand in hand, because——"

"And I now agree with you on that, so you needn't make your speech to me, Mary!" It was Mrs. Jeffers' turn to stop the flow of words. "But you see, we have just illustrated my point, in a way. Wherever there are groups of women gathered together for one reason, and that is their interest in their own advancement, then you should talk about the subjects nearest to their hearts— women's suffrage and dress reform. But when you speak to an audience that has come together first of all to see the famous Dr. Mary Walker from America, and to hear about her experiences, you waste your breath in trying to win them over to these causes, worthy though they be."

"You talk women's rights to them," Mary objected.

"I used to discuss women's rights whenever I found a half-dozen people together," Mrs. Jeffers confessed. "But now I pick and choose my audiences. Oh, I know we have to do a certain amount of work that could be considered pure crusading, but it is more important that we spread our energies among the women who will in turn recruit other women. Only in that way can we hope to begin the legislation that will one day make it possible for women to vote and have something to say about the world."

"I suppose you're right, Millicent," Mary said doubtfully. "I must admit that my talk runs too long as it is. The Reverend Denison gave me some interesting figures the other day on the length of time an audience's attention can be held. It seems to be scientific information, so I suppose one must heed it and conduct oneself accordingly. Well, I'll rework my material and do as you suggest—as a trial only, you understand."

She found that there were benefits in cutting apart her long speech and concentrating on one subject at a time. For one thing, it gave her a chance to add to each segment. She had always enjoyed searching out facts to back up her remarks, and she realized that these facts added to the weight of her talks. As she worked over her speeches, the thought came to her that she had here the makings of a book that she would write when she had the time, with each speech supplying the material for a chapter.

Even though she had followed the advice of her friends, Mary was never able to leave out entirely either dress reform or women's rights, no matter what the subject at hand nor what group she was talking to. But she did her best. If her tongue sometimes ran away with her, she had still tried.

In June, after having concentrated on the lecture platform for several months, she left for Paris with the Denisons, to visit the Paris Exposition of 1867. She wrote long letters home to her family, letters that for a time contained no references to Mary Walker and her mission in Europe. She was entirely caught up in the gaiety of the French city that was crowded with people from all over the world who had come to the Exposition.

"I saw the Sultan of Turkey!" she wrote home. "What a resplendent costume, and on a man! And I was at the Exposition with my dear friends when the news was spread about that Maximilian had been shot in Mexico. It was a dramatic moment, let me tell you, for all of us, because someone went up to Emperor Napoleon III, who was in the middle of a speech, with the Empress Eugenie beside him—she is most beautiful, as I think I've said before—and whispered in his ear, and he stopped talking and left the platform without another word."

Everything, Mary thought, was exciting in Paris. She insisted on seeing all the sights while she was there, and also on attending a big dinner given by and for Americans in Paris on the Fourth of July. The dinner turned out to be unexpectedly dull.

"These people should be celebrating not only our Independence, but the end of the Civil War, and they should be remembering the men on both sides who gave up their lives in that war," she fretted to herself. "I had expected more of the occasion, I must say."

Without warning she was on her feet. Over her black costume she wore a sash of Stars and Stripes—Mrs. Denison, she had noticed, had tried hard not to look at her guest, and especially not at that sash—and in her strange garb she marched smartly to the head of the table, quieted the startled crowd with a flutter of her small hand, made a terse little speech about the soldiers and sailors of America, kissed the flag and, unperturbed, returned to her place.

She saw with amusement that the Denisons' faces were crimson.

"Stirred things up, didn't I?" She chuckled. "Dull before."

Paris in general had many other opportunities to observe her, as she trotted about sightseeing and visiting hospitals, and the people for the most part seemed to like her. Mary herself thought nothing of being gaped at, but Mrs. Denison nervously noted the temper of the people who stared after them on the street, and she reported thankfully to her husband that although people did smile a great deal, they seemed friendly toward their little American friend.

"Just the same, I will be glad to get her back to England," she declared to her husband. Mary walked into the room in time to hear the remark, and Mrs. Denison smiled at her warmly. By now she knew the little doctor didn't mind being discussed in the least.

"Why, my dear?"

"Because—well, these people are so—so French!" Mrs. Denison explained.

"So they are," her husband agreed. "And so they should be, since they are French. I think there is nothing to worry about. Everyone has been very kind, indeed. Don't you feel that way yourself, Mary? And even the Empress, they say, has asked about you and is interested in your notions on dress reform."

"If I could only see her, talk to her!" Mary cried. Enlisting the glamorous Empress in the cause would indeed be a boost for dress reform, but even Mary realized she was probably the only person in the world who could picture Eugenie in bloomers! "But I have tried to, and they tell me it can't be done. Oh well."

They went back to England late that month, and in August Mary traveled to Liverpool and took a ship for home. She had seen a great deal of England and Scotland; she had, she felt sure, accomplished much in the way of winning recruits and recognition for her causes; and she had been seen by a great many people. It had been, she acknowledged gleefully to herself, quite a year.

11

a new career

Washington!" Mary said. "Really. So provincial."

"I can remember," Laura Whiting reminded her, "when you thought Washington was the center of the world."

"I was wrong. I hadn't seen anything of the world then."

They were sitting in the stuffy little parlor of Mrs. Schenk's boarding house. Mary had, of course, given up the little house owned by Harry Whiting when she left for England, and when she returned she was told not only that it had been let immediately, but there was no other property available. Sometimes she suspected that Harry refused her as a tenant because of her past record of failure to pay, but Laura said nothing about it. At least she had cleared up her debt to Harry, and there were other houses to be had, although she couldn't seem to find one. Temporarily she was in a rooming house that reminded her of her first months in Syracuse—the same dingy wallpaper, the same smell of cooking, even a view of an alley from her small window.

That didn't matter. What did matter was that although she had come home expecting to be acclaimed by everyone, and sought after to speak all over the country, no one seemed to be the least interested in her.

"Why, Miss Walker, I haven't seen you in some weeks." "Have you been away for a time, Dr. Mary? You weren't at our last meeting, I believe." "You haven't been ill, have you?" People had scarcely missed her, much less learned of what she had accomplished in England. Mary couldn't believe it. Only Laura knew of her achievements, because Mary had written to her about them, but Laura, for some unaccountable reason, hadn't sent her letters to the press or even told the other women about what she'd done. "Jealous," thought Mary. "Of course, the poor, silly woman is green with envy."

"Will you revive your practice?" Laura asked her, and Mary detected a note of derision in the query.

"I may, in time," Mary replied calmly. "But at the moment I have other plans." Laura looked at her curiously but didn't press the point, and Mary, disappointed, changed the subject. The fact was, she had decided that if the English liked her talks so much, the Americans would enjoy them even more. If the story of her enforced stay in Castle Thunder had kept the English quiet and attentive, what wouldn't it do to Americans! In the three years since the war's end, the personal experiences of the men who had fought through the grim battles and lived to tell the tale had been recounted over and over. By this time people had forgotten their harrowing stories. Now she, Mary Walker, would come along with a fresh slant, the unusual approach of a woman who had been, for a time, a political prisoner, and all of that dormant interest would be revived. Surely, she thought, the time was exactly right.

Working on her own, she managed to get some bookings in New England and in New York State, and worked out a three-month circuit. The audiences were never as large as she hoped, but they were for the most part in favorable moods.

"Do you know what they did in one city?" Mary gleefully reported to Laura at the end of the tour. "At the last minute one of

the fuddy-duddies in the church where I was to speak found out
that I wore trousers, so they insisted the lecture be given elsewhere. Somehow they scraped up another auditorium—a sorry
thing it was, too, small and dark with a stage that creaked every
time you shifted from one foot to another. And because the people
who wanted to hear me hadn't all learned about the change, they
came trooping over from the church a few at a time, clumping in,
whispering and talking. It was most exasperating, but it served
them right."

"I would think you were the one who suffered," Laura suggested.

"I did, in a way. It's most annoying to a speaker, of course. And
some people never even got to the auditorium at all, poor things."

"You are very sure people want to hear you," Laura said acidly.

"They pay for tickets, don't they?" Mary retorted.

Still, after the three months were over, she reviewed the tour
and reluctantly admitted to herself that she couldn't get enough
money from such a schedule. The engagements were too far apart,
and there weren't enough of them to make it pay.

"Now what?" asked Laura, who always seemed to be on hand to
ask Mary questions she either couldn't or didn't want to answer.

"I'm going south," Mary told her firmly.

"To talk about having been in one of their horrid prisons? I
hardly think they'll take to that," Laura said with a shrill giggle.

"No, no," Mary said impatiently. "The women there have a
right to learn about what's going on. I spent enough time with
Southern women to understand them. I'll talk on women's rights
and dress reform. They'll love it."

"But how are you going to arrange such a trip? You can't arrive
in a town and say, 'Here I am, come to spread the gospel to all you
good women.'"

Mary looked at Laura with distaste. She deplored Laura's flip-
pant attitudes. "Since I am committing myself to discuss women's
rights, I can work through the groups that have been formed for
the purpose of forwarding those rights," she said pompously. She
didn't bother to explain to Laura that speaking to a group gath-

ered together because of a predisposition to the subject at hand
was an easy way out. The groups were avid for the information she
could give them; she would be, therefore, a predestined success.

So she was on the road again and she was, as she had foreseen,
accepted everywhere she went by the women who were waiting
for the kind of inspiration she had to give. Twice she had brushes
with the law when policemen, outraged by her costume, dragged
her to judges, both of whom got rid of her quickly. Newspapers
printed doggerel about her, which boys on the street picked up
and chanted, but Mary smiled over it all. It did no harm, she
thought, and the publicity must inevitably work for her in time.
Let them have their fun.

Presently she forgot everything else in her excitement over an
invitation that had reached her from Port Gibson, a town in Mississippi. She was invited to help organize a group of women who
would devote themselves to the cause of women's rights, and they
would pay handsomely if she would visit the town and give them
the help they needed so badly. Mary was delighted. This, she
thought, was true recognition. At the risk of offending others, she
cancelled two or three speaking engagements, packed her bags,
and headed for Mississippi as fast as she could go.

It seemed a long trip from Kansas City to Vicksburg, and the
last thirty miles from Vicksburg to Port Gibson seemed to Mary to
take forever, but throughout the interminable trip she was intent
on her plans for the new society. She drafted them as she rode on
train and steamboat, plans based on the groups she had worked
with in America, with a few improvements suggested to her by the
operation of English societies of the same type. By the time she
reached Port Gibson she was well satisfied with her neat outline,
and even wondered if she couldn't, after successfully launching
this chapter, begin organizing on a national scale. How busy she
would be!

There was no one to meet her, but then of course no one knew
just when she would arrive. She checked in at the first hotel she
saw, a small, dismal place where the men stared at her and at her
trousers and dusty, wrinkled frock coat in a way she didn't like.

First of all she asked for help in locating the Miss Reed who had written to her.

"What address? There's no such street, ma'am, not in this town."

"But look, here it is. Here is the letter," Mary said curtly. "See for yourself."

"No such street. But don't take my word for it, if you don't want. Town office is down the street. Want someone should take you?"

Mary looked around at the watchful faces and said hastily, "No, thank you, I'll find it." She snatched her letter from the desk clerk's hand and marched out of the lobby, feeling every eye on her. I must, she thought, find another place to stay at once.

She was so indignant that she scarcely bothered to look around her at the lovely little town on Bayou Pierre, a town that Ulysses Grant had said was "much too beautiful to burn" when he passed through it six years before. The white frame houses were neat and sedate under the afternoon sun, and the streets were shaded by oak trees evenly spaced. But Mary flew along without looking around. She was anxious to get to work.

She had little trouble in finding the town office. It was, as it happened, also a doctor's office. Mary's heart lightened considerably. She had at least an educated man to deal with, and a fellow practitioner. That should make things much more agreeable.

The doctor kept her waiting until all of his patients had gone. As Mary had looked around at the crowded waiting room, she had wondered what it would be like to have one's services in such demand, and for a moment her thoughts went back wistfully to Rome, New York, when she and Albert had shared a practice and a waiting room that was often as well filled as this one.

"I do think of that—that villain at the oddest moments," she said to herself, and then dismissed him from her mind. Her divorce decree had come through a few weeks before, and she was now legally free of the unwanted ties of her marriage. There was certainly no further cause to think of Albert.

The man in the doorway stood looking at her. His contempt for her costume was undisguised. Mary stood, drawing herself up as tall as she could, and said, "I am Dr. Mary E. Walker, of Washington, D.C., and I am not a patient, sir. I am here because I was told at the hotel that in some official capacity you could advise me as to how to find a person for whom I am looking. It is Miss Mary L. Reed, who wrote me this letter."

The man glared at her from under bushy eyebrows, then took the letter from her hand. He did not invite her into his office, nor did he suggest that they sit down; he just stood there, resting his big bulk against the frame of the door as he read the paper he held.

Then he lowered it and turned his gaze on Mary once again. She stood her ground. She was sure from the scowl on his face that he was going to make some stupid comment on her costume, but she was ready for it. She would endure it quietly, and then urge him to return to the matter at hand.

"Perhaps you had better come in, Miss—er, Doctor," he said in a surprisingly gentle voice. She followed him into the office, and when he waved a huge hand at a chair, sat down in it. "I—well, I'm afraid, to be blunt about it, that you have been hoaxed," he said, staring at her from under his heavy brows. "Very much afraid, and I must say I'm sorry."

"But I don't understand. The letter—you read the letter."

"Ma'am—I mean Dr. Walker—I have lived in this town all of my life, and I suppose I know pretty much everybody in it. I surely know all of the streets. There never was such a street in Port Gibson, not ever, and I am sure of it. I have never heard of this woman; I doubt if there is such a person, and I wager your reply, if you sent one, is waiting unclaimed at the post office this minute."

Mary felt her head reeling. "But they—she promised me six hundred dollars!" she cried. "I have come all this way, all the way from Kansas City where I was addressing——" Her voice died away. Instinctively she knew that the man sitting uneasily behind his desk was telling the truth.

"I see," she then said quietly. "Thank you for your time."

"I will send for your things at the hotel," he told her. "You would not want to stay there, not even overnight. Mrs. Graham and I will be happy to have you as our guest until you feel yourself up to moving on."

Mary accepted the hospitality gratefully. She wondered at first if she could ever rise above the cruel joke that had been played on her. "Why?" she asked herself. "All the way here, and—who would do such a thing?" Her mind flicked to Ruth, the tearful roommate in Castle Thunder. Ruth had come from Mississippi, although she'd never mentioned which town it was. But she would have no reason to hate, would she, the woman who had shared the awful, cramped quarters with her? Mary's head ached with the wondering, but her recuperative powers were great, and the next morning she announced, in her usual voice, "I will go to Vicksburg today. I have friends there, people I met during the war, and they will arrange a lecture for me, I know. I thank you for your hospitality, which was offered at a moment when I had serious need of it, but I must keep going."

Both Dr. and Mrs. Graham urged her to stay.

"Since you are so concerned with the education of women, you would be interested in our Female College—it is older than you are! We would be glad to show it to you. And some of our lovely old homes, and the new ones too—Windsor, as fine as any other in the South, I'm sure. And Canemount—there are many. And the famous Natchez Trace——"

Mary remained firm about leaving. She wasn't quite sure, but she thought she saw a gleam of relief in Mrs. Graham's eyes. The poor woman had tried to avoid looking at Mary from the first moment, and Mary knew that her costume was an embarrassment to her hostess. For once she didn't feel contempt. The Grahams had been kind to her.

The lecture tour went on. First to New Orleans, then to Texas, and in June of that year she returned to Washington. There was no doubt now, even in her own mind, that she was unable to support herself by lecturing, and she was perplexed about this. She had heard of men and women who made as much as forty or fifty thousand dollars a year on the lecture platform. Why couldn't she do better financially? Whether it paid well or not, she loved it and

so she still agreed to take on an engagement whenever it was offered, going once as far as Ottawa.

In the meantime she began to work on the book she had been
thinking about for some time. It was a compilation of her lectures,
in a way, and she found that it fell easily into place, as she had
expected it to. She called it *Hit*.

Her first book didn't make any more money for her than her lecture tours had done, but she could now add the word "author"
after her name. One unexpected by-product of being a published
author was the appearance at the end of *Hit* of an advertisement
for "Alvah Walker's Water Elevator." Her father had been forever
tinkering with devices for easing work around the farm, and his
greatest success had been this invention, which he had patented in
1868. His advertisement stated that his water elevator had
achieved the "highest premium awarded at the New York State
Fair and two county fairs" and it was described as capable of
bringing water from the bottom of the deepest well and of dump-
ing it into a pail immediately, with no waiting. As Mary had so
often heard him describe his invention enthusiastically, the page
stressed the fact that a small child could now draw water with the
help of the elevator, which made it possible for four buckets to be
drawn and emptied from a well twenty feet deep and located
eight rods from the house—and all this in less than a minute.

The invention didn't make much more money for the inventor
than the book did for the author, but both Mary and her father
were pleased with the visible linking of their talents. Mary had
always admired her father's inventiveness, and occasionally she
tried her own hand at the same game. She had actually patented
one of her ideas, the placing of a neckband inside a man's shirt
collar to protect the skin from the irritation of collar buttons.

"Men!" she wrote to her father gleefully. "The poor creatures
have been wearing shirts and collars for generations, and all the
while suffering from the minor tortures of collar buttons. It took a
lady wearing the same garment to free them!" At times like this
Mary neglected to class her father with "men," just as when she

spoke contemptuously of women, she forgot that she was one herself.

These were the exciting years in the campaign for women's rights. Mary, back in Washington, found herself speaking at meetings where she met, as a fellow speaker, Lucy Stone—the same Lucy Stone whose example she had followed in refusing to use Albert's name. She also worked with Susan B. Anthony, Belva Lockwood, and others. She had the edge on most of them in a way, because she could speak with authority of the progress of women's rights in England, having observed them first-hand. It made her proud to stand on a platform and tell her "sisters" about what she had seen in Europe.

"You've come a long way from your family farm," said her good friend Belva Lockwood, and Mary agreed.

Things seemed to Mary to be going so well because of the support from these other women that she was dismayed when she found them becoming discouraged by the remarks made about them in the press, or discovered one or another of them in tears and threatening to discard bloomers altogether because of having been ridiculed on the street.

"What do you care what those idiots think?" Mary demanded crisply. "I've been stared at most of my life, but it hasn't changed me any. Things aren't accomplished too easily in this world, you know. If having some horrid little boys make fun of you upsets you, just fasten your eyes on your goal and you won't hear them or even notice them any more. *I* don't."

Washington attracted them all as it did Mary, and what one of these indomitable women didn't think up, another one did. Mary found herself caught up in a whirlpool of speech-making, of developing classes for women in law and medicine, and of doing everything possible to focus public attention on the subject of votes for women. Everywhere she went Mary Walker was a hit, partly because she wore her strange costumes with great ease, thanks to having worn them consistently for so long, and because her very smallness seemed to tickle the fancy of the people who saw her. They liked her curls, too, she knew that, although they were becoming less important to her now. Her reputation as a speaker had grown to the point that even when she wasn't scheduled as part of the program, she was usually called up on the platform by popular demand.

"There's one thing about you, Mary," her co-workers remarked frequently, and not always without a touch of acid in their voices, "you never lack for words."

Even Mary knew it was inevitable that the solid front of militant women would break up. Each an individualist, stubborn and forthright, sooner or later they must start stepping on each other's toes. She felt that some were lagging behind, and told them so, and she watched with dismay and frustration as one after another dropped out of the ranks and returned to more peaceful lives. Last of all came the end of her friendship with Mrs. Lockwood. Hard as her friend Belva had worked with her, Mary had never quite reconciled herself to the fact that Mrs. Lockwood would not wear bloomers or trousers, and on her side Mrs. Lockwood continued to point out to Mary that her odd costumes held back the advancement of women's rights instead of helping it along.

Just because she warred with one after another of her friends, Mary hadn't the slightest notion of giving up any of her pet causes. She still went to all the conventions, although she was no longer a delegate or an officer, and when people shouted for her, quite often she wasn't recognized by the platform chairman and had to be content with standing up and bowing to the delegates. They couldn't prevent her from doing that much. She had, after all, been at these conventions for more than forty years and there were many who remembered her. She continued to visit groups of people whenever she could—at fairs and at picnics, wherever they gathered. She tried to register to vote in her home town and was turned away. She printed handbills, prepared a pamphlet on "Woman's Franchise," and went right on badgering congressmen. In fact, when she was eighty-three she would be back in Washington again, still fighting. Even her enemies, and she had made many, later admitted that it was a shame she didn't live until women's votes became a national reality.

"What a production," someone said, "she would have made of waltzing up to that ballot box and depositing her own acceptable, legal, female vote!"

12

the lonely years

Money," Mary told her sister, "has plagued me all my life."

"You mean the lack of money," Aurora corrected her. "I know, Mary, and I fear the problem has been your failure to settle down as a doctor. You have always left your practice to go rushing off to one convention or another, or to run around Washington getting signatures on one of your gigantic petitions. Like that one you told me about—what was it, two hundred feet long?"

"Two hundred and forty." Mary nodded. "But, Aurora, a lot of us worked on that; I didn't do it by myself, you know."

"But you did some of it, probably more than your share, and it took time. How could you expect to acquire patients and treat them properly, if you were not even in your office?"

"I have always done what must be done," Mary replied primly. "Someone had to do these things. Most people sit back quietly and allow those scoundrels to spend public funds for mountains of ice in Alaska, or steal Hawaii from its people, or whatever foolish notion pops into someone's head. I am not made that way. I try to right the wrongs and inequalities of this world."

"I know," Aurora observed mildly, "and I admire you for it. But unfortunately no one sees fit to pay you for the hours you spend righting these wrongs."

"Or trying to," Mary added bitterly.

Her lack of money often made her bitter these days. Ever since the war she had been trying to get a pension for herself. Her eyes, damaged during her Army service, had caused her trouble ever since, and her benevolent government had given her eight dollars and fifty cents a month in recognition of her injury—a sum that she considered both useless and insulting. All through the years, as she worked diligently on one cause or another, she was forever struggling, as a sort of sideline, to get some money for herself. She often boasted of the number of bills she had sent to Congress, all seeking well-earned money for Dr. Mary E. Walker.

"Harry says," Laura Whiting told her after hearing the figures quoted a tiresome number of times, "that your diligence is greater than your powers of persuasion, my dear Mary."

Mary bit back a retort, and as usual when she was faced with an unanswerable criticism, fingered the medal she always wore. It, at least, was tangible proof of recognition.

"If you would just dress sensibly——"

"Sensibly! My dress is——"

Laura hurriedly interrupted the flood. "If you would dress normally, then," she said sharply, "as other women do, I'm sure people would be more inclined to listen to you."

"My manner of dressing and my being entitled to a pension are not in any way related," Mary snapped.

"But they are, in people's minds. Surely you must see that. Harry says——"

"Harry says, Harry says. What do *you* say, Laura Whiting, or must you parrot your precious Harry with every breath?"

Laura left in a huff, and Mary regretted her ill-considered comment. Laura was a poor thing, she thought, but she was a friend, and ever since Mary had broken with Belva Lockwood and the others she had lived a more solitary life than ever. Also, there were fewer causes to involve and exhilarate her these days. She was only half-aware that the spaces between her efforts were becoming longer and longer, and in those spaces she found herself growing listless and broody. But then when something came along—a petition, a reason to storm a congressman's office, or a meeting to attend—she came alive once more, throwing herself into whatever it was with the same old fervor.

Because of those empty spaces, and because of her chronic lack of money, Mary finally determined to get a government job of some kind. She knew better than to try to set up a practice of medicine again—she had left that behind her at last. After several false starts and months of being put off, she was given a job in a mailroom in the Department of the Interior.

These days her everyday costume was a black broadcloth suit made like a man's, and she had now cut off her curls and wore a tall silk hat on her short hair. And she always carried a cane. Accustomed to the stares of the world, she paid little attention to those of her fellow workers in the mailroom. Although she didn't exactly go out of her way to be friends with them, she sometimes gave them bits of medical advice whether they wanted it or not. She didn't like them anyway, and she liked the job even less, considering it much beneath her capabilities.

An unexpected development that came directly from her experience in the mailroom was the "invention," for so she called it, of three devices designed to speed mail on its way. She claimed complete responsibility for the new card created as a receipt for registered letters, which of course served to relieve the senders' uncertainty about their delivery. She also worked out an improved way of handling third-class mail, which she presented with an expression akin to contempt to the head of the mailroom.

"It is time," she said waspishly, "That someone did something about the unwieldy handling of our mails. You may take this and claim it as your own idea, if you like. Who knows, you might get a medal!"

The man accepted the hand-written pages from her, stared at

the thin little figure in its masculine attire with ill-disguised dislike, and said, "Thank you, Miss Walker."

"Dr. Walker," Mary said mechanically. From the start the man had refused to use her correct title.

She turned away, but looked back quickly in time to see him drop her careful plan into the wastebasket. Abashed by the angry glare she directed at him, he sheepishly fished out the papers and spread them across his desk. He never mentioned the episode again, but Mary had the satisfaction of seeing her plan put into action.

Later she single-handedly, or so she always claimed, saw to it that a law was passed that permitted the names and addresses of the senders to be placed on packages, thus saving thousands of undeliverable pieces from winding up in the post office storerooms.

"People!" she exclaimed to Aurora. "People are very inefficient. When you come right down to it, most people don't think at all, or at least no more than is required of them in the course of a day."

Because of her indifference to the position and to the mailroom itself, the job finally came to a close, and once more she was at loose ends. Her sister Aurora urged her to return to the farm, which their father had left to Mary when he died in 1880.

"You could write some more, Mary," she insisted. Mary's book *Hit,* published in 1871, had been followed in 1878 by another called *Unmasked, or the Science of Immorality.* Neither had sold well, but Aurora knew that Mary had enjoyed writing them and that she liked to think of herself as an author. "At home you'll have time, and peace and quiet, too, for writing."

"Maybe." Mary looked doubtfully at her sister. "But first I'm going back on the platform for a while. Oh, don't worry about the financial end—not this time. I'm being highly practical, as you'll see. I have signed with an agency—the kind that routes acts around the country."

"Acts! What do you mean? Not those side-show affairs that they have everywhere now? Why, Mary, you will be a—a freak!"

Mary chuckled. "It won't be the first time the term has been

applied to me," she said. "No indeed, Aurora, you should not look
at it that way. See here, I am sending them some lines about myself to be used in advertising me."

Aurora looked at the paper Mary held out to her and gasped.
"You wouldn't let them say such things about you?"

"Why not? They're true."

Aurora looked at Mary's stubborn face and gave up. "Contrary
Mary still, I see. One could never accuse you of modesty. Really,
Mary! Well, considering the handsome sum they agree to pay you,
I suppose it's all right."

When Mary came back from her tours she quite obviously enjoyed reliving each trip as she told Aurora about it.

"And there," she said, at the end of the third tour, "That repays
every cent I ever borrowed from you. I wish Lyman was still alive
to see me give you the money, Aurora. Your husband always dis-
approved of your lending it to me."

"How did you know that? He didn't mind really, it was just
that—"

"Oh, I could tell. I never saw much of Lyman, but he had a way
of looking at me when the subject of money came up. I knew."

"Lyman set great store by being financially successful," Aurora
said placidly. "That is all. You enjoy your speaking engagements
even more than what they pay you, don't you, Mary? I mean, you
don't do it just for the money?"

"Of course I don't. I love every minute of it. And in spite of what
you think, appearing on the same bill with a Punch and Judy show
doesn't bother me a bit. People like entertainment, and it's the
entertaining acts that pull them in. When they're there, I have my
chance at them. It's as simple as that."

"Well, you must know what you're talking about." Aurora
sighed. "You've been at it long enough."

"And there have been so many changes," Mary said eagerly. "I
believe what I say must be having more effect than before, perhaps. And much of it has to do with what's going on in the world
today. Bicycling—you have no idea, Aurora. I haven't seen one
on the road here, but in many places there are clubs, and the

members go out together on all-day bicycle rides. It has become popular, let me tell you."

"Women, too?"

"Of course. And even with the new frame they've designed, women can't ride wheels in long full skirts. That would be out of the question. At first, they tell me, they tried tucking them up in some manner, but the poor silly creatures discovered that they were revealing far too much ankle and leg. So, inevitably, and we could have told them they'd come to it, of course, they have taken to bloomers. Some still insist on divided skirts that look like any other skirt when worn standing or just walking, but allow proper freedom for riding wheels, but that's only a step toward real bloomers. I've had to cut whole sections out of my speech on dress, because the people who hooted and jeered at my ideas forty years ago take many of them for granted now. It's—exciting."

"And now," Aurora commented wisely, "you are aching to be away and at it again. But you have just come home, Mary. And I'm sure Mother is glad to have you here."

Mary frowned. "She doesn't like having me leave," she admitted. "Says it's too lonely at the house alone, and she has tried to make me promise to stay. Of course I can't do that. I have suggested that she move in with Alvah next door. You'd keep an eye on the place for me, wouldn't you, Aurora? I know my brother won't—he has a chip on his shoulder where I'm concerned."

Aurora promised goodheartedly to watch over Mary's farm even though it meant extra work. It was too bad, she reflected, that Mary and her brother didn't get along, but they hadn't for years, and their relationship was growing worse all the time.

Once when Mary returned from a long swing through the east, she found Alvah's horses stabled in her barn. Without bothering to consult anyone, not even Alvah himself, she simply turned them out.

"What right had you to do that?" demanded Alvah, after he and the neighbors had at last rounded up the animals. "I think you *are* crazy, Mary."

"What right had you to use my barn without my permission?"

"I am taking care of Mother. She is supposed to live in Father's house, which means with you. But you won't stay home and she doesn't like being there alone. And she's supposed to have half the income from that farm, and there isn't any income. So I have taken over responsibility for her. The least you can do is allow me to stable my horses in your barn."

"If I tell you you may, you may. But I haven't done so." Mary turned back to the house. "I hear you thought of contesting Father's will," she tossed over her shoulder. "Lucky for you that you thought better of it." And that had been the end of the little friendship that had once existed between Mary and her brother.

Nowadays Mary saw more and more of Evvy Blake. "Well, she does live next door," she explained to herself. "So does Alvah, but after all, there's no point in seeing *him*."

Evvy's husband had been killed in a farm accident and Evvy's children were married. The older two lived at some distance, but Louise and her lazy, good-natured husband had moved into Evvy's house and presumably took care of Evvy and the farm.

"Farm!" said Evvy contemptuously. "That Ralph doesn't know the meaning of the word. If he plants seeds one day, he's through for the year. He thinks the crops come up and pick themselves, that one does."

"So your children haven't been such a great comfort to you after all," Mary said slyly.

"Of course they have!" Evvy cried. "It's just that lazy good-for-nothing Louise married."

Mary shook her head. "Poor Evvy," she remarked. "Stuck here on a farm that's going backward. And I've had such a full life. Oh, Evvy, you can't believe what I've done, what I've seen, where I've been."

Evvy cast a swift look at Mary's costume, but turned away without a word. Mary, looking at her old friend's face, thought she detected an expression of sadness there. For a moment she experienced one of her rare moments of regret, feeling sorry that she had so often tried to remind Evvy of her success and to point out the great gap between her own busy years and Evvy's dull and fruitless life.

She said good-by to Evvy gently and walked slowly home. She wished that her relationship with Evvy had been more comfortable. Perhaps if she watched her own acid tongue, she could bring about a warmer friendship. Mary badly needed a friend now. She had always had Aurora, who had stood by her over the years, but now Aurora was dead and Mary felt very much alone. She had lost more than a sister, she had lost a friend, confidante, and tower of strength.

When Aurora died, Mary was sixty-eight, and now she found herself at last tied to the farm for good. For a while she thought of converting the place into a school for young women. After all, her own schooling and that of her sisters and brother had begun here, so there was a tradition to base it on. The school would, she decided, teach young women the fine art of housekeeping, so that when they married they would be ready for the job. Farmers' wives in particular, she said, needed to know a great deal about farm life. Mary would open a training school for wives; what she planned was *not*, as the press termed it, an "Adamless Eden," made up of young females who would swear never to marry. That she was hardly qualified to teach anything about farming or being a wife never crossed Mary's mind.

A later plan for the farm was to convert it into a sanatorium, and to the sanatorium for the cure of consumption she would add a school created to study its prevention. She even advertised it, but there was no response, so she gave it up.

But there always seemed to be something around the corner. Just as one absorbing idea was discarded, another took its place. This time she was rescued by a letter from an old acquaintance that lifted her out of a mood of depression and gave her something to crusade for again.

"But, Mary, do you really know this woman? A princess? Really!" exclaimed Evvy when Mary ran over with the news.

"Of course I know her. Eleanor was a nurse, and I met her more than once when I was in the Army," Mary retorted. "She was a pretty good nurse, although she'd had no real schooling. But then, most of them hadn't."

"How did she get to be a princess?"

"Oh, I don't know," Mary said indifferently. "She married someone, a Turk or a Greek—I think it was a Greek. He was a prince, so that made her a princess. Simple."

"Are you going to Vermont to get her? Mary, do you really think you should?"

"She needs help. Someone's trying to get her money away from her. It says so in the letter."

Evvy sighed. "I suppose you know what you're doing," she said after a thoughtful pause.

"I usually do," Mary agreed promptly.

Mary went to Rutland and found her friend too ill to be moved. She nursed her and her maid, who was also ill, until they were fit to travel. Then she took them to her farm, and for a while things worked out well. Eleanor, the Princess, was grateful and the maid tried to show her gratitude by helping out, although she made it evident that farm kitchens and the other inconveniences of rural living weren't exactly to her taste. But—inevitably—the Princess and Mary quarreled. To Mary's annoyance, instead of leaving town or, better yet, New York State, the Princess somehow talked Louise Bush, Evvy's daughter, into letting her board on the Blake farm, where she held court in Evvy's parlor and told all the neighbors about how poorly she had been treated by Mary.

Mary blamed Evvy's daughter. Louise made no pretense of liking Mary. From the first time they had met in Evvy's kitchen, Louise's pale eyes had stared at her mother's friend coldly. When Mary called on Evvy, Louise invariably disappeared. When the two women met on the street in the village, Louise gave a curt little nod, and if Mary inquired after her mother's health, she replied in monosyllables.

Mary strongly suspected that Louise was behind the move of her titled guest. Undoubtedly there had been rumors around town to the effect that Mary and the Princess had had a falling-out. Louise Bush had snatched at the opportunity, Mary believed, suggesting that the Princess and her maid install themselves in Evvy's house.

"I hope she enjoys feeding them," Mary thought with a wry smile. "Perhaps she thinks she'll get a free hired girl in that maid, but she has something to learn there!"

Convinced that Louise was at fault, Mary quickly recovered from her first reaction to Evvy's harboring of the enemy. Louise's brief triumph wouldn't last long, she was sure, because the Princess and her regal ways would try the patience of anyone who tried to harbor her.

With the Princess gone from her house and, soon, from her mind, Mary suddenly found that she had nothing to do. As usual, however, life took care of the lull for her. There was a murder case in New Hampshire that was taking up everyone's attention, and Mary decided the murderer was, instead of the prisoner who was being tried, a former hired man of her own. She went to Concord and made such a nuisance of herself that she was jailed for three days, and then instructed to leave New Hampshire and not to come back. The hired man promptly sued her for slander.

By the time Mary got home, the Princess had left town, and Evvy and Mary resumed their precarious friendship.

"Mary, whatever made you think you knew more than the law?" Evvy remonstrated.

"Law. What does it know? I've known more than the law a good many times, and don't you forget it. I have no use for the law or the courts or any of it. They've convicted the wrong man. That poor creature—can you imagine what it would be like to be accused of a murder you didn't commit?"

"But this slander suit—Ralph says that man wants ten thousand dollars from you!"

"He won't get it. I haven't got it, for one thing. But even a court wouldn't be that stupid."

Evvy shook her head in disbelief. She expected the worst, but when the trial was over, it was Mary who had been right.

"Six cents!" she chortled. "Instead of ten thousand dollars. Now there's one jury that had its wits about it!"

During the trial the newspapers had, of course, made much of

Mary's eccentricities, and surely as her life moved toward its end the eccentricities became more pronounced. The young people growing up, knowing nothing of her Civil War achievements or the good honest work she had done in the interest of women's rights, saw only her costume and heard exaggerated tales about her. Practical jokes were played on her, too, but Mary went her way.

With Aurora, her staunchest friend, gone, and at odds with her brother, Mary might have turned to Vesta and Luna for companionship, but they had by now drifted as far away from her as Cynthia had long before. Her closest family contacts were, actually, with her two maiden aunts in Massachusetts. She had seen them occasionally, stopping off in their Greenwich home whenever her lecture tours took her near enough to make it possible, and she still wrote them frequently.

In 1895 her Aunt Mary, after whom she had been named, died. Mary packed up her things and hurried to Greenwich.

"I must go and see to Aunt Vashti," she said importantly to Evvy, as she dropped off the key to her house on the way to the railroad station. "Aunt Mary was the leader of the two, you see, and Aunt Vashti will be lost without her. My aunts were devoted, and I must do what I can to take Aunt Mary's place."

Evvy, who liked to poke fun at the strange names in the Walker family, tittered at the mention of Aunt Vashti and remarked, "Certainly the cousins or whatever they are that live around there can take care of the old lady. Why should you travel all the way to Massachusetts, for pity's sake?" Evvy's shrewd little eyes turned to Mary sharply. "There wouldn't be a little bit of money involved, would there, to make you so interested all of a sudden?"

"Certainly not!" Mary snapped. "You know very well my aunts have always been fond of me, and I of them. That's a shameful thing to say." But she found Evvy's comment embarrassing. It was true that she had done a little thinking about what could be done with the money Aunt Mary was bound to have left her.

When she installed herself in the house, telling Aunt Vashti to leave everything to her, Mary discovered that Evvy was not the only one to entertain suspicions about her motives. Her cousin appeared at the door one day, and, obviously not relishing his assignment, said that a family conference had been held and it had been decided that someone was to suggest that Mary leave Greenwich and return to Bunker Hill Road.

"Unhappily, I have been appointed spokesman," he said politely. "We thank you for your interest, but we are perfectly able to take care of Aunt Vashti, and——"

"Take care of her!" Mary exclaimed. "Henry Woods, for all I know you will put an end to the poor woman's life. Such things as go on here, who is to say who is behind them? That milk, for example. It doesn't fool me; I'm a doctor of medicine and I know about these things. I wouldn't be all surprised if there's arsenic been put in it. I wouldn't drink it for all the world, nor will I let my aunt touch it—the poor, unsuspecting creature."

"Vashti never drinks milk," he said shortly. "But—arsenic! Really, Cousin Mary! And it's all over town that you told Joe Green, who took you in his hack the other day, that there are men wearing masks after you."

"I am convinced that there are people interested in the possessions in this house," Mary said darkly. "People who should be ashamed of themselves. And they're employing such methods, hoping to frighten me, no doubt."

Henry, bewildered, took his leave, but he returned later with a brother and a brawny young nephew. Mary couldn't keep the three big men out of the house, although she tried, and she stood by helpless but extremely and shrilly vocal as they walked about peering into cupboards and dresser drawers. It was Henry who found the courage to look in one of Mary's own traveling bags, where he discovered all of the aunts' best silver.

"I put it there for safekeeping!" Mary cried out fiercely.

"We will keep it safe," Henry said quietly. "And we must again ask you to quit this house, Dr. Walker."

Mary went back to Bunker Hill Road, but in a short time she returned and began diligently to pack up the household furniture.

The place was to be sold, and Aunt Vashti's things had been moved into Henry Woods's home, where the old lady had been installed. Henry found Mary hard at work, and he noted at once that some of the boxes were addressed to herself. Again he asked her to leave, and he locked the door behind her.

"I thought I had the best of him, just the same," Mary said to Evvy later, acknowledging that she had failed in her efforts to outwit the Massachusetts branch of the Walker family. "I wrote to some of the cousins who don't live in Greenwich and who therefore aren't in this conspiracy that appears to exist, and I asked them to send me copies of Aunt Mary's will, and to suggest that I be appointed administratrix of the estate. But they wouldn't do it. I'm going to keep at it though. All I've done for that family—it's time someone did a little for me."

"You won't get anywhere," Evvy told her. "You wait and see."

This time Evvy was right. Mary not only didn't get what she wanted, although she went to court about it, but she was charged the court costs. And she lost, once and for all, the good will of her Massachusetts relatives.

"Oh well," she said philosophically. "Now I'll get back to work."

Her work wasn't exactly demanding, but she kept busy. She still made speeches, on occasion—for women's suffrage, for pensions for widows, on the causes of tuberculosis, and in 1912, when she was eighty, she made a speaking tour of western New York.

In 1917 something happened that would have crushed many people, but Mary was still contrary enough to brush it off. The Board of Medal Awards—"that should be spelled m-e-d-d-l-e," Mary snorted when she heard about it—was reviewing awards made during the Civil War and they made up their minds that the medal given to Dr. Mary E. Walker was a mistake. Mary took off for Washington and pleaded eloquently, but the Board refused to change its opinion.

"I earned it; I will continue to wear it," she said, stamping out of the room. Some of her inquisitors looked mighty uncomfortable, she noticed, as she turned and gave them all one last, scathing glance.

And she did wear it, or rather she wore two, because ten years before she had been given a second medal with the original design somewhat altered. The new medal was supposed to replace the old one—but Mary wore them both.

The only visible effect her trip to Washington had on Dr. Mary was the result of a fall on the Capitol steps. The injury didn't seem serious at the time, but it was later thought to have contributed toward her death. In the meantime she kept busy. Immediately after the declaration of war on Germany, she fired off a cablegram to Kaiser Wilhelm, offering her farm on Bunker Hill Road as the site of a peace conference. She never received an answer from the gentleman, but as usual her act got good notices from the press. And the war itself did something for her—it accomplished overnight what she had been working for all her life. Because huge numbers of women now went to work in the factories, clothes underwent a change. Skirts were shortened, and often exchanged for pants. In the same year New York State women were given the right to vote, with the Nineteenth Amendment to the Constitution of the United States, which would be passed two years later, being all that was required to make it national.

Always greatly interested in herself, for the last few years she had been arranging her home so that it was becoming, in effect, a museum to herself, with pictures and scrapbooks on display.

"Oh, Mary, who wants to see all this—this rubbish!" Evvy exclaimed. Evvy had suddenly grown very fat and getting about was a problem for her, but Mary had hitched up her horse and driven over to fetch her friend. It pleased her to push and shove Evvy's bulk into the wagon, as she herself skipped about with the wiry agility she had displayed all her life.

"Everyone," Mary retorted. "I'm famous. Wait and see, crowds will flock here. You never did appreciate me, Evvy Barnes."

In 1918 Mary became ill, and when she was discharged from the hospital in September, there was no one to care for her. Aurora, of course, would have been at her side every minute and would have nursed her devotedly, but Aurora was not there, nor were the other sisters who presumably would have cared for her under the circumstances.

So it was Evvy Blake who, overriding her daughter's objections, insisted that Mary be taken straight from the hospital to her farm, and there Mary stayed until the end came on February 21, 1919.

To anyone who would sit still at her bedside during the last months, she was always glad to tell of her accomplishments, reminding her hearer that there had been a time when presidents and generals and cabinet members had been glad to meet and listen to her. She kept her medals, both of them, always within reach, usually pinned on her pillow or herself, and fingered them constantly. Even Evvy now and then made the stupendous effort required to creep painfully from her room to listen to the stories she'd heard many times before.

"They tried to take my medal away, the Indian givers," Mary muttered frequently. "But they couldn't do that, could they? They reckoned without Mary E. Walker, when they tried to pull a trick like that. Did you know what they always called me when I was little? Contrary Mary. Or sometimes just Contrary. 'Contrary, Contrary, supper's ready!' I can hear their voices now. I guess I had to live up to it somehow. A lot of those generals and congressmen, they found out I could be as contrary as the next one. More so, some of them must have thought. Of course I've been called a lot of other things, too—a newspaperman once said I was a 'self-made man.' I had to laugh at that myself, I did!

"I haven't any complaints. I didn't get a lot of things that were due me, but I had a pretty good life, useful and more exciting than most women's, let me tell you. I've been to England and France—they had two great ladies over there and I saw them both, Queen Victoria and Empress Eugenie. Nobody told them to go hide in their houses and leave the running of the world to the men. If they'd only listened to us about dress reform. . . .

"And in this country—why, when you stop to think of it I've talked to millions of people in my day! They listened to me, too. And now the things I tried to drum into all those heads are coming true—pants on women, the vote, everything. I did my bit, I guess. And I guess it pays to have someone around who can be contrary!"

When Mary Walker died, she was eighty-six years old. She was buried in her best black suit, and at the simple funeral in the Walker homestead they draped over her casket the American flag she had served and loved. She had been colorful as well as contrary, and she had had her share of admirers, but Mary Walker had seldom inspired affection. It was with a slight sense of surprise that a muffled sobbing was heard from the back of the room during the service.

When it was over, and the family went out into the cold air, they looked curiously at Luna's granddaughter.

"But, Beth," said the girl's mother in surprise. "I didn't know you cared so much for Aunt Mary!"

"I didn't—I mean, it isn't that," sniffled the young woman. "It's —well, I'm so ashamed. The last time I saw her on the street I pretended I'd forgotten something back at school, and I ran back for it. It was just that I couldn't bear to have the others—well, you know. I should have been *proud* of her!"

Even Mary would have been touched at the tribute.

They took her out to the cemetery and buried her in the frozen ground. When they returned to the Blake house, Evvy, who had made the greatest effort but found herself unable to get out of bed for the funeral, inquired about the gravestone.

"What did they put on it?" she asked her daughter, Louise.

"It says just Mary, Mamma. Why?"

"Nothing." Evvy looked up at the stained ceiling over her head. "Nothing, Louise. No reason. I've been lying here thinking. I was wrong all my life about Mary Walker. Jealous of her every minute, I was, and bound not to let on to her that I even liked her, much less kind of admired her. I'm probably the only person in the world that even figured out how she hated being short—the only runt in a tall family. It made a scrapper out of her, the way I see it. And I realize now that she paid for every single thing she got— paid by being laughed at and not understood. I never saw, really, that she was a generous woman, inside those funny clothes. She worked and worked to make the world a better place for the rest of us. Not to attract attention or make people pat her on the back, like I used to think, but for the rest of us.

"Just Mary on the headstone, eh? Well, they should have put it all."

"Mary Walker? Or the doctor part?"

"No, no, her real name was what her family called her, Contrary Mary. They should have put it there for all to see. Well, it doesn't matter. She always said herself she was a legend in her own time. Maybe she was. People will always remember her, I guess, and when they do, they'll remember Mary the way she wanted to be and the way she was all her life—*quite* contrary."

author's note

The framework of dates and events in Mary Walker's life is as accurate as possible, and for the most part taken from the detailed and carefully documented biography by Charles McCool Snyder, but Evvy, Laura, Celia, and other friends and acquaintances are pure invention. So too are all conversations and letters.

Throughout I have been concerned with *why*—not only the possible reasons behind her crusading for dress reform and women's rights, but of the little things. Why, although educated and intelligent, did she appear to be unsuccessful as a doctor . . . why would she allow herself to be booked as a sideshow attraction . . . why would she make a spectacle of herself in the middle of a church service or at a state dinner . . . why did she drift into and out of a brief and unsatisfactory marriage. . . .

One can, of course, only guess at how she really felt. For all her eccentricity and bravado she was, after all, a human being with feelings, and she was humiliated many times and must have been hurt much. But she was often a warm and even generous person, for all she was self-centered, and I've tried to show her that way.

BIBLIOGRAPHY

Bill, Alfred Hoyt, *The Beleaguered City.* New York, Alfred A. Knopf, 1946.

Dictionary of American Biography, Vol. XIX, edited by Dumas Malone. New York, Charles Scribners' Sons, 1936.

Ketchum, Richard M., *National Portrait Gallery. American Heritage Magazine*, August, 1968, Vol. XIX, Number 5.

Memorial History of Syracuse, New York, edited by Dwight H. Bruce. Syracuse, H. P. Smith & Co., 1891.

Mississippi, A Guide to the Magnolia State. American Guide Series, Federal Writers Project. New York, The Viking Press, 1938.

National Cyclopaedia of American Biography, Vol. XIII. New York, J. T. White & Company, 1906.

New York, A Guide to the Empire State. American Guide Series, Federal Writers Project. New York, Oxford University Press, 1956.

Snyder, Charles McCool, *Dr. Mary E. Walker, the Little Lady in Pants.* New York, Vantage Press, 1962.

Strong, Gurney S., *Early Landmarks of Syracuse.* Syracuse, The Times Publishing Company, 1894.

Tennessee, A Guide to the State. American Guide Series, Federal Writers Project. New York, The Viking Press, 1939.

Walker, Mary E., *Hit.* New York, The American News Company, 1871.

Woodward, Helen Beal, *The Bold Women.* New York, Farrar, Straus and Young, 1953.